Obento
Deluxe

Workbook

Sue Xouris
Kyoko Kusumoto

THOMSON
★
NELSON

Australia · Canada · Mexico · Singapore · Spain · United Kingdom · United States

THOMSON

NELSON

Level 7, 80 Dorcas Street
South Melbourne, Victoria, 3205

Email nelson@thomsonlearning.com.au
Website http://www.thomsonlearning.com.au

First published in 2004
10 9   8   7   6
15 14 13 12 11 10 09 08

Editor: Tina Hutchings
Publishing editor: Olive McRae
Designer: Yuri Tanabe
Cover designer: Yuri Tanabe
Production controller: Selina Brendi
Illustrations by Yuko Fujita, Mami
Cover illustration by Yuko Fujit.

Disclaimer
Every effort has been made to trace and ac
this come to the attention of those concern
they contact them so that proper acknowle
reprint of this book.

Obento Deluxe contents

Meet the *Obento* kids!

Nakayama Gakuen is an international school in Japan attended by both Japanese students and students from around the world. All the international students are being hosted by Japanese students, except for Ben, who has lived in Japan for some time with his family.

まつだ ゆき
Yuki Matsuda
Age: 14 years old
Home town: Tokyo

ケイト・ヘンダソン
Kate Henderson
Age: 12 years old
Home town: Sydney

エマ・ジェニングズ
Emma Jennings
Age: 12 years old
Home town: Auckland

ベン・サマーズ
Ben Summers
Age: 14 years old
Home town: Perth

トニー・クルーズ
Tony Cruise
Age: 14 years old
Home town: Vancouver

ハジョーノ・スダーガー
Harjono Sudarga
Age: 13 years old
Home town: Jakarta

さとう ゆうすけ
Yuusuke Sato
Age: 14 years old
Home town: Tokyo

もりやま たかこ
Takako Moriyama
Age: 13 years old
Home town: Tokyo

ふくだ けんいち
Kenichi Fukuda
Age: 14 years old
Home town: Kobe

かきかた

Practise writing these characters in the boxes using the correct stroke order.

Handwritten character

Printed character

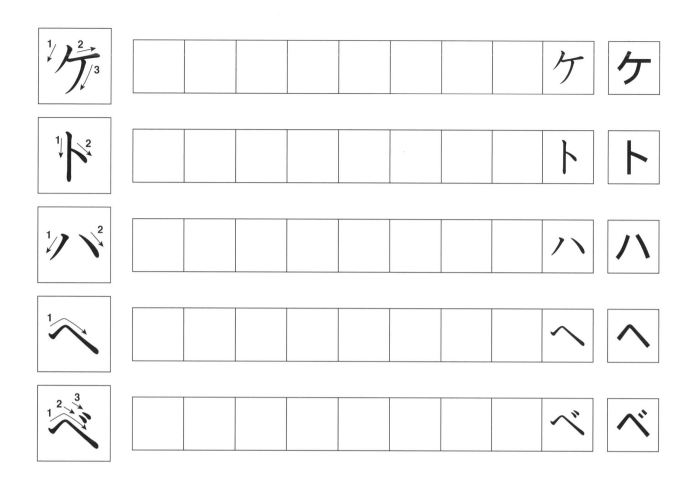

| | | | | | | | | | ケ | ケ |

| | | | | | | | | | ト | ト |

| | | | | | | | | | ハ | ハ |

| | | | | | | | | | ヘ | ヘ |

| | | | | | | | | | ベ | ベ |

1

Using coloured pencils, indicate four examples each of hiragana, katakana and kanji on this Japanese magazine cutting.

ニウェアで んおしゃれ

天特集／人気NO・1スタイル徹底

牧瀬里穂 ファッシ インタビ

わかった！今年の

この秋の４大アイテム、ジージャン・中丈スカート・バンダナ

ファッション、カタログ／この秋、何を買ったらいい

前髪いじり３分間

上げる・分ける・巻く、の３変化の美微妙な使い分けでキミの

ヘア特集／通学前の三分でできるイメージチェンジ

をつかむSMAP

男のコの欲しいプレゼントNO・1手編みのセーターを初め

彼のこころ

2

Use the key below to colour in this picture and reveal the hidden image.

Green: お
Brown: ハ
Black: き
Orange: エ and た
Light blue: ゆ and ケ
White: ま
Dark blue: こ
Red: さ
Pink: な

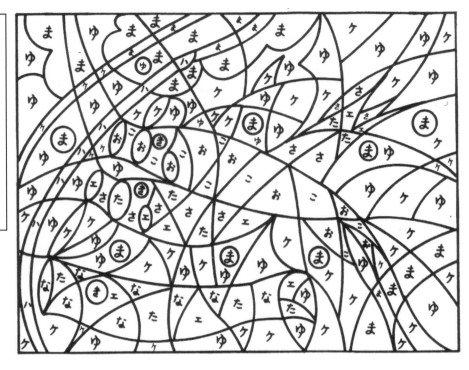

3

Emma, Kate and Harjono are taking their study of hiragana and katakana very seriously. They have become human kana! Write the kana they have become in the boxes provided.

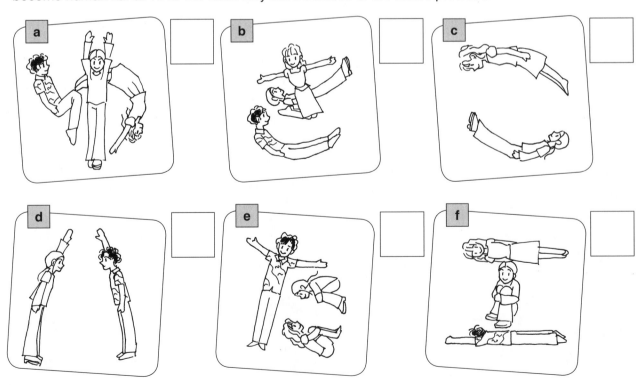

Home stay list

エマ .... ゆき
ケイト .... たかこ
ハジョーノ .... ゆうすけ
トニー .... けんいち

4

Match the Obento students with their hosts.
Refer to Mr Nakamura's list to help you.

a	
b	
c	
d	

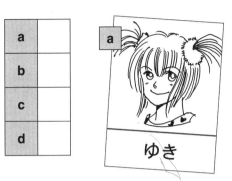
a
ゆき

b
ゆうすけ

c
たかこ

d
けんいち

2
エマ

3
トニー

1
ケイト

4
ハジョーノ

5

Some of the students' name tags were left on Mr Nakamura's desk during lunchtime and, unfortunately, coffee was spilt all over them. Help him repair the tags by completing the stained characters. Use his class list to help you.

クラス リスト

ハジョーノ

たかこ

ベン

けんいち

ゆうすけ

ケイト

ゆき

トニー

エマ

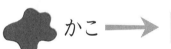 かこ → ☐ か こ

マ → ☐ マ

イト → ☐ イ ト

ジョーノ → ☐ ジョ ー ノ   ン → ☐ ン

うすけ → ☐ う す け   んいち → ☐ ん い ち

き → ☐ き   ニー → ☐ ニ ー

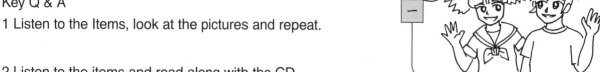

一 Greeting and farewelling

Key Q & A

1 Listen to the Items, look at the pictures and repeat.

2 Listen to the items and read along with the CD.

一	まきさん、こんにちは。
	あさみさん、こんにちは。
二	あさみさん、おはよう ございます。
	よしくん、おはよう ございます。
三	あきおくん、さようなら。
	あさみさん、さようなら。
四	なかむらせんせい、また あした。
	あきおくん、また あした。

7

Listen to the tape and complete the table. The first one has been done for you.

	Kate is talking to	It's morning	It's after 11	They're saying goodbye
a	Yuusuke & Emma		√	
b				
c				
d				
e				

8

Go around your class to find students who can say one of the phrases on the survey forms below. Ask them to sign their initials in the space provided. You have four minutes to complete the survey.

Phrase	Initialled by
Say good morning.	
Say hello to the teacher.	
Say goodbye.	

Phrase	Initialled by
Tell your friend you'll see her/him tomorrow.	
Say hello to your friend.	
Say goodbye to everyone.	

9

Nakamura Sensei is a bit forgetful. He often confuses the names of his students. Help him to sort them out by matching each student with his/her correct name.

a	
b	
c	
d	
e	
f	
g	
h	
i	

a　ゆうすけ

g　トニー

h　ベン

e　ケイト

b　ハジョーノ

f　ゆき

c　たかこ

i　けんいち

d　エマ

10

Colour in all the squares that contain katakana in the maze below. Then, look for these words and phrases hidden in the maze and fill in the missing characters.

a	Mr Nakamura	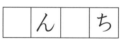
b	Hello.	
c	Yuki	
d	Yuusuke	
e	Good morning.	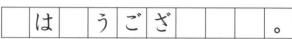
f	Takako.	
g	Goodbye.	
h	See you tomorrow.	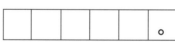
i	Everyone	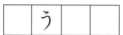
j	Kenichi	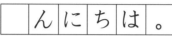

a □ □ む ら □ ん □ □

b □ ん に ち は 。

c □ □

d □ う □

e □ は □ う ご ざ □ □ □ 。

f □ □ □

g □ □ う □ ら 。

h □ □ □ □ □ 。

i □ □ □ ん

j □ ん □ ち

エ	ハ	ケ	エ	ゆ	き	ハ	ケ	エ	ハ
お	は	よ	う	ご	ざ	い	ま	す	ト
ケ	エ	す	ハ	ケ	た	エ	た	ハ	べ
さ	け	ケ	エ	ハ	か	ケ	あ	エ	ケ
よ	ハ	ケ	エ	ハ	こ	ケ	し	ハ	ゆ
う	エ	ハ	ケ	ト	け	エ	た	み	き
な	か	む	ら	せ	ん	せ	い	な	ト
ら	ハ	ケ	エ	ハ	い	ト	ケ	さ	ハ
エ	ケ	こ	ん	に	ち	は	エ	ん	ト

二 Asking someone to do something and responding

Key Q & A

1 Listen to the items, look at the pictures and repeat.

2 Listen to the items and read along with the CD.

一	みなさん、きいて ください。
二	あさみさん、みせて ください。
	ちょっと まって！
三	あきおくん、たって ください。
四	まきさん、ドアを あけて ください。
	はい。

12

Listen to the instructions on the tape. Match each instruction with the most appropriate situation shown in these pictures by writing its number in the empty speech bubble.

Look at picture A of Mr. Nakamura's classroom as he enters it. He would like to begin his lesson but his class is not ready yet! Listen to his instructions on the tape, then draw the necessary changes to the classroom in picture B. You might like to make notes in English as you listen.

14

You enter an ancient Japanese castle in search of a magic samurai sword. Follow the path and give the right instructions to find the sword. Try role-playing this search in your classroom.

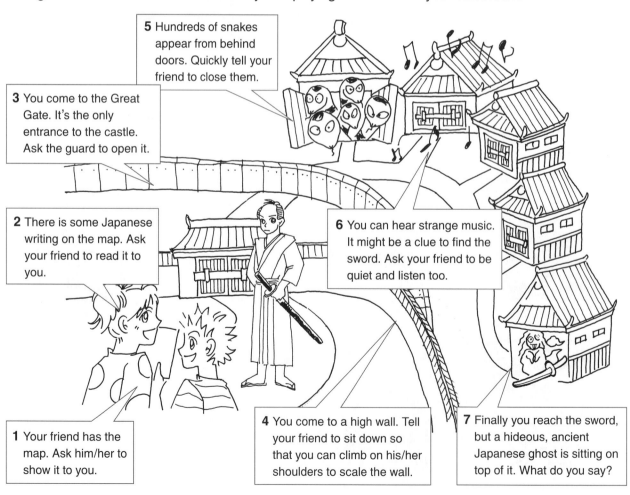

5 Hundreds of snakes appear from behind doors. Quickly tell your friend to close them.

3 You come to the Great Gate. It's the only entrance to the castle. Ask the guard to open it.

2 There is some Japanese writing on the map. Ask your friend to read it to you.

6 You can hear strange music. It might be a clue to find the sword. Ask your friend to be quiet and listen too.

1 Your friend has the map. Ask him/her to show it to you.

4 You come to a high wall. Tell your friend to sit down so that you can climb on his/her shoulders to scale the wall.

7 Finally you reach the sword, but a hideous, ancient Japanese ghost is sitting on top of it. What do you say?

Colour in all the squares that contain katakana in the maze below. Then look for these words hidden in the maze and fill in the missing characters.

a   Just a moment    ち ょ っ と ☐ っ て く だ ☐ ☐ 。

b   everyone   ☐ ☐ ☐ ん

c   Please stand up   ☐ っ て く だ ☐ ☐ 。

d   Listen please   ☐ ☐ て く だ ☐ ☐ 。

e   Show me please   ☐ ☐ て く だ ☐ ☐ 。

f   Look, please   ☐ て く だ ☐ ☐ 。

g   Sit down, please   ☐ わ っ て く だ ☐ ☐ 。

h   Kenichi   ☐ ん ☐

i   Be quiet!   ☐ ず ☐ に

j   Write it please   ☐ ☐ て く だ ☐ ☐ 。

k   Read it!   ☐ ん で

まどをあけてください

し	ず	か	に	エ	ケ	み	み	な	さ	ん
ト	ハ	ヘ	ト	ニ	た	せ	て	ハ	ケ	エ
ち	ょ	っ	と	ま	っ	て	く	だ	さ	い
ト	ヘ	エ	き	い	て	く	だ	さ	い	け
ケ	ト	ハ	ヘ	ト	く	だ	さ	エ	ヘ	ん
す	わ	っ	て	く	だ	さ	い	ケ	ト	い
ト	エ	ト	ケ	ハ	さ	い	ケ	ト	ヘ	ち
よ	ん	で	ハ	か	い	て	く	だ	さ	い
エ	ケ	ト	ト	ハ	エ	ト	ヘ	エ	ト	ケ
ま	ど	を	あ	け	て	く	だ	さ	い	ト

16

Complete the following characters.

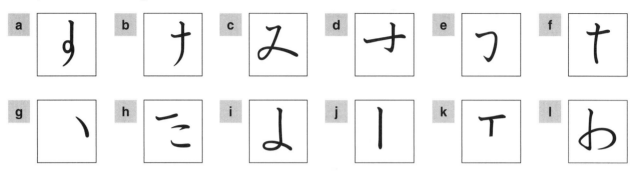

Write your favourite four hiragana and your favourite two katakana.

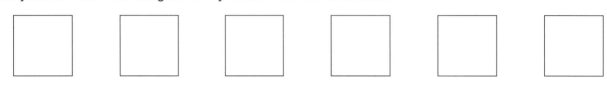

17

Find as many hidden hiragana, katakana and kanji characters as you can on this treasure island.
Colour them in different colours, then write them in the empty boxes.

どんなあじ

三 Asking someone's name and introducing yourself

Key Q & A

1 Listen to the items, look at the pictures and repeat.

2 Listen to the items and read along with the CD.

おなまえは？	一	まき です。どうぞ よろしく。
	二	わたしは あさみ です。どうぞ よろしく。
	三	ぼくは あきお です。どうぞ よろしく。

19

Listen to the Obento students introduce themselves. Write their names in English in the order in which you hear them.

a _____ e _____

b _____ f _____

c _____ g _____

d _____

20

Form circles of five students each. Using the pattern below, go around your circle asking the person next to you who they are.

Person 1

こんにちは。わたしは _____ です。おなまえは？

Person 2

わたしは｜_____ です。どうぞ よろしく。
ぼくは　｜

When you have been around the circle once, see how quickly you can go around again. Have a race with the other groups to go around your circles. Don't forget to call out やったー！ when you have finished!

Fill in the empty speech bubbles in the pictures with the number of the appropriate response from the list.

1 エマ です。

2 せんせい、おはようございます。

3 また あした。

4 さようなら。

5 こんにちは、ゆきさん。

6 おなまえは？

Japanese writing

There are three separate writing systems which are used to write Japanese. They are **hiragana**, **katakana**, and **kanji**.

Hiragana *characters look round and curly and are used to write Japanese words.*

KATAKANA LOOK ANGULAR, LIKE STRAIGHT LINES WITH POINTY BITS AND ARE USED TO WRITE WORDS WHICH COME FROM OTHER LANGUAGES and

Kanji look like little pictures and have a meaning, like a whole word.

My name is written in katakana and looks like this

おなまえは？   です。

onamae wa?   desu.

What is your name?   I'm

Ask your teacher to write your name for you in Japanese in the box above then practise writing it yourself until you can do it without looking. Use the katakana chart in the back of the Workbook to identify the katakana in your name.

ごちそうさま

I can:

- ☐ greet and farewell students in my class and my teacher
- ☐ ask someone's name
- ☐ say my name and introduce myself
- ☐ use a title after people's names
- ☐ give someone at least eight instructions
- ☐ say the names of the Obento students
- ☐ write the hiragana characters あ、い、お、か、き、け、こ、さ、し、す、せ、た、な、ま、み、ゆ、よ
- ☐ recognise some key hiragana words
- ☐ write the katakana characters エ、ケ、ト、ハ、ヘ、ベ
- ☐ recognise some key katakana words
- ☐ know why it's important to listen and guess
- ☐ say what hiragana, katakana and kanji are and what they're used for
- ☐ say what an obento is
- ☐ say what the sections in this book are called and what they're used for
- ☐ say at least six things about the life of a high school student in Japan.

おべんとう クイズ

1 Circle the correct answer. (8 marks)

A おはようございます is a greeting you would say:
- in the morning
- after 11.00 am
- when you go home

B さようなら is used when you want to say:
- Hello.
- Pleased to meet you.
- Goodbye.

C If you see your friend at lunchtime you could say:
- おはようございます。
- こんにちは。
- さようなら。

D たって ください is a way of asking someone to: **sit down / look / stand up**

E If the wind was blowing in through the door and your homework was flying everywhere you should ask your friend to:
- すわって ください
- ドアを しめて ください
- ドアを あけて ください

F You say みせて ください when you want someone to:

listen/ look at something / show you something

G Your teacher might say しずかに when he/ she wants you to:

be quiet / stand up / sit down

H If someone told you to ドアを あけて ください you would:
- close the door
- show them something
- open the door

2 Match these words and phrases with their English translation. (11 marks)

A おはようございます。	Yuki
B こんにちは。	Mr Nakamura
C さようなら。	Kate
D また あした	Good morning
E たかこ さん	Harjono
F ゆき さん	Hello
G なかむら せんせい	Emma
H ゆうすけ くん	Goodbye
I エマ さん	See you tomorrow
J ハジョーノ くん	Takako
K ケイト さん	Yuusuke

3 What would you answer if someone asked you おなまえは？ Write your answer in Japanese. (1 mark)

_____ です。

4 Complete these sentences. (5 marks)

A There are ___ writing systems in Japanese.

B The names of the Japanese Obento students are written in _____.

C The names of the international Obento students are written in _____.

D There are ___ hiragana and ___ katakana characters.

5 Write the first character in the Japanese word for: (5 marks)

good morning __ / goodbye __ / stand up __ / sit down __ / write it __

/30

かきかた

Practise writing these characters in the boxes using the correct stroke order.

Handwritten character

Printed character

1

Using the hiragana you already know, write down these Japanese names.

a Takeshi 　⬚⬚⬚　　**e** Masao 　⬚⬚⬚　　**i** Akemi 　⬚⬚⬚

b Kimiko 　⬚⬚⬚　　**f** Machiko 　⬚⬚⬚　　**j** Yumiko 　⬚⬚⬚

c Michiko 　⬚⬚⬚　　**g** Masumi 　⬚⬚⬚　　**k** Taka 　⬚⬚

d Akiko 　⬚⬚⬚　　**h** Sachiko 　⬚⬚⬚　　**l** Chiyumi 　⬚⬚⬚

2

一 Counting up to 20

Key Q & A

1 Listen to the items, look at the pictures and repeat.

2 Listen to the items and read along with the CD.

一	はじめ！
	一、二、三、四、五。
	おわり！
二	はじめ！
	一、二、三、四、五、六、七、八、九、十。
	おわり！
三	はじめ！
	一、二、三、四、五、六、七、八、九、十、十一、 十二、十三、十四、十五。
	おわり！
四	はじめ！
	一、二、三、四、五、六、七、八、九、十、十一、 十二、十三、十四、十五、十六、十七、十八、十九、二十。
	おわり！

3

Help these busy bees find their flowers by following the numbers from 1 to 10. Then count how many of each number are left in the puzzle. Write your answers in kanji numbers in the tally box.

Example: 一 ⟶ 四

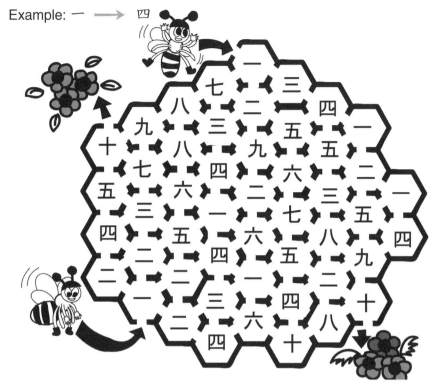

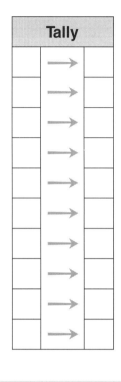

	Tally	
	⟶	
	⟶	
	⟶	
	⟶	
	⟶	
	⟶	
	⟶	
	⟶	
	⟶	
	⟶	

4

How many of the following items do you have in your classroom? Count them aloud in Japanese and write down the correct kanji number next to each item.

A windows ☐   **C** posters ☐   **E** blue pencil cases ☐

B blackboards ☐   **D** desks ☐

5

It all adds up!

A 五 + 三 = ☐   **E** 八 + 六 = ☐   **I** 七 + 五 = ☐

B 六 + 七 = ☐   **F** 十 + 十 = ☐   **J** 三 + 二 = ☐

C 九 + 四 = ☐   **G** 二 + 四 = ☐   **K** 八 + 九 = ☐

D 四 + 三 = ☐   **H** 一 + 七 = ☐   **L** 五 + 一 = ☐

6

It's maths time! Fill in the missing numbers in these sequences.

A | 一 | 三 | 五 | 七 | | |

B | 二 | 五 | 八 | | |

C | 二 | 三 | 五 | 六 | 八 | | |

D | 一 | 三 | 二 | 四 | 三 | | |

E | 十 | 九 | 八 | | | | |

7 どんなあじ

二 Asking someone's age and responding

Key Q & A

1 Listen to the items, look at the pictures and repeat.

2 Listen to the items and read along with the CD.

なんさい ですか。	十一さい です。
	わたしは 十三さい です。
	ぼくは 十四さい です。

8 On Teacher's CD track 20

Listen to the conversations and fill in the ages of each person under their picture.

| 1 | 2 | 3 | 4 | 5 | 6 |
| | | | | | |

はなしましょう

Listen to the conversations and write the ages of each of the people mentioned.

1	Maki			2	Yoshi	
	Asami				Akio	

Then, use the text on page 23 of your student book to role-play it with your partner.

10

Go around your class to find six students who are the same age as you. Write their names below. Use the question なん さい ですか。 When you find them, say あっ、わたしも or あっ、ぼくも。

わたしは
ぼくは [   ] さい です。

なまえ	
1	4
2	5
3	6

11

Match these people with their correct age.

A	
B	
C	
D	
E	

5	三さい

4	一さい

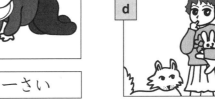

1	二十さい

2	十五さい

3	二十九さい

12

Write down the ages that come immediately after the ones given.

A 十三さい		さい
B 二十九さい		さい
C 五さい		さい
D 十さい		さい
E 十八さい		さい

F 六さい		さい
G 十五さい		さい
H 三十さい		さい
I 十四さい		さい
J 二十七さい		さい

13

These people are celebrating their birthday. Find out how old they are by counting the candles on the cakes. Then write down their ages.

Example: Masami

A Akemi

B Taka

C Naoko

D Takeshi

E Chiseka

14

Listen to the conversations and write, in English, the phone number of each person speaking.

1	**4**
2	**5**
3	**6**

三 Asking someone's telephone number and responding.

Key Q & A

1 Listen to the items, look at the pictures and repeat.

一 9773-0210

二 8632-0499

三 9432-8765

2 Listen to the items and read along with the CD.

でんわばんごうは？	9773-0210 です。
	8632-0499 です。
	でんわばんごうは 9432-8675 です。

16

Listen to the messages on Takako's answering machine. Match the callers with the correct phone number.

A	
B	
C	
D	
E	

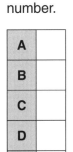

1 670-2244

4 764-8011

5 864-0492

3 894-0492

2 731-8461

6 773-0210

7 763-2966

c Chieko

d Harjono and Yuusuke

a Carla

b Ben

e Mr Nakamura

17

Listen to the directory assistance information and write down the correct telephone numbers for these people.

A Tanaka Saburo

B Kawakami Kaoru

C Yamada Hitomi

D Fujimoto Yoshio

おしょうゆ クイズ タイム

a If you're thinking about what to say next you say:

- あっ！
- えーと …
- えっ！

b You say がんばって when you want to:

- wish someone luck
- correct yourself
- say hello

c If something was absolutely incredible you could say:

- すごーい！
- すし！
- すみません！

d You say おたんじょうび おめでとう

- at Christmas
- on Mother's Day
- to say Thank you
- on your friend's birthday

e You say どうぞ when:

- you give something to someone
- you take something from someone
- you answer the phone
- going home after school

f When you meet someone for the first time, you say:

- はじめ
- おはようございます
- はじめまして

g When you answer the phone you say:

- もしもし
- よしよし
- すしすし

h Number these words for thank you from most polite 1 to casual 3.

- どうもありがとう ☐
- ありがとう ☐
- ありがとうございました ☐

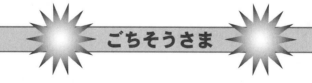

ごちそうさま

I can:
- ☐ Count to 20
- ☐ Ask someone's age and answer when someone asks me my age
- ☐ Ask someone's telephone number and answer when someone asks me for my telephone number
- ☐ Read and write the numbers from 1 to 20 in kanji
- ☐ Read and write the hiragana て、は、ほ、わ、で、ば、ぼ
- ☐ Read the words and expressions: わたし、ぼく、でんわばんごうは？
- ☐ Identify different people in Japanese society
- ☐ Understand a little about Japanese lifestyles
- ☐ Use a few tricks for remembering Japanese numbers

おべんとう　クイズ

1 Circle the correct answer (4 marks)

a なんさいですか　is a way of asking:
- someone's telephone number
- someone's age
- someone's name

b おたんじょうび　おめでとう is a way of saying:
- Happy Birthday
- Thank you
- I'm pleased to meet you.

c なんさい　ですか。
Circle the answer that applies to you.
十一さい　です。
十二さい　です。
十三さい　です。
十四さい　です。
十五さい　です。

d Which of the Obento students might say:
ぼくは　十四さい　です。
- たかこ　さん
- ケイト　さん
- けんいち　くん

2 Arrange these numbers from smallest to largest. (4 marks)

A 五　八　三　七　四　六

B 十四　十一　十三　十　十二

C 九　十五　十一　十七　十三

D 二　十六　十二　八　十　九

3 Write the following ages in kanji and kana. (5 marks)

6		13	
17		15	
9			

4 What are these questions asking you? Write your answers in Japanese below. (6 marks)

a おなまえは？ _____

b なん　さい　ですか。 _____

c でんわばんごうは？ _____

5 Write these phone numbers in numerals. (6 marks)

a 五二六 - 二四一一 _____

b 七八三 - 九二〇五 _____

c （〇三）九三三六 - 四八一二 _____

d 三九〇 - 五一六三 _____

e 九四八 - 一二三四 _____

f （〇九）三八六 - 七八七八 _____

6 Fill in the missing kana. (5 marks)

a なん ＿＿ で ＿＿。
b でん ＿＿ んごうは？
c ＿＿ようござ ＿ ます
d わた ＿。
e ＿く

かきかた

Handwritten character

Printed character

Practise writing these characters in the boxes using the correct stroke order.

1

Find the hiragana and katakana characters hidden on this island. Colour them in different colours and then write them in the spaces provided.

じ	う
ひ	す
む	に
オ	ま
カ	よ
ア	め
ト	え
	ら

2

You are the social director of an international convention in Tokyo. It is your job to organise interpreters for the foreign delegates. Identify the non-Japanese names by circling them. Remember, Japanese names are usually written in hiragana (or kanji) and foreign names are written in katakana.

A たなか	**F** ボーダー	**K** やまだ	**P** おおたに
B ミッチェル	**G** こにし	**L** ウィリアムズ	**Q** コンスタンティーノ
C いのうえ	**H** たかはし	**M** せき	**R** よしだ
D しみず	**I** わたなべ	**N** にし	**S** つちや
E リム	**J** ジョーンズ	**O** デービッドソン	**T** ソーンクラーフト

3

Write these names in Japanese.

A Mr Ishikawa ☐☐☐☐

B Ms Seki ☐☐

C Mr Takahashi ☐☐☐☐

D Mr Ideishi ☐☐☐

E Ms Sakai ☐☐☐

F Ms Tanaka ☐☐☐

G Mr Akai ☐☐☐

H Ms Oki ☐☐

4

Complete these words with the correct katakana.

A Canada ☐ ナ ダ

B America ☐ メ ☐

C Indonesia ☐ ン ド ネ シ ☐

D Australia ☐ ー ☐☐☐☐

E New Zealand ☐ ユ ー ジ ー ☐ ン ド

F Kate ☐☐☐

G Harjono ☐ ジョ ョ ー ノ

H Emma ☐ マ

I Tony ☐☐ ー

5

一 Asking where someone is from and responding. Saying your nationality.

Key Q & A

1 Listen to the items, look at the pictures and repeat.

2 Listen to the items and read along with the CD.

| どこから ですか。 | 日本<small>にほん</small>から です。日本人<small>にほんじん</small> です。 |

| どこから きましたか。 | オーストラリア<small>おーすとらりあ</small>から きました。オーストラリア<small>おーすとらりあ</small>人 です。 |
| | ぼくは インドネシア<small>いんどねしあ</small>から きました。インドネシア<small>いんどねしあ</small>人 です。 |

6

Listen to the どんなあじー　はなしましょう and answer the questions in English.

1 Where is Mr Nakamura from and what nationality is he? _____

　Where is Kate from and what nationality is she? _____

2 Where is Harjono from and what nationality is he? _____

　Where is Takako from and what nationality is she? _____

3 Who is asked a question about Emma? _____

　Where is Emma from and what nationality is she? _____

　Where is Takako from and what nationality is she? _____

Now, act out the conversations in pairs.

7　　**On Bonus CD**

1 Listen and number the flags from **a** to **f** according to the conversation.
2 Then, match up the written word by putting its number in the appropriate box.

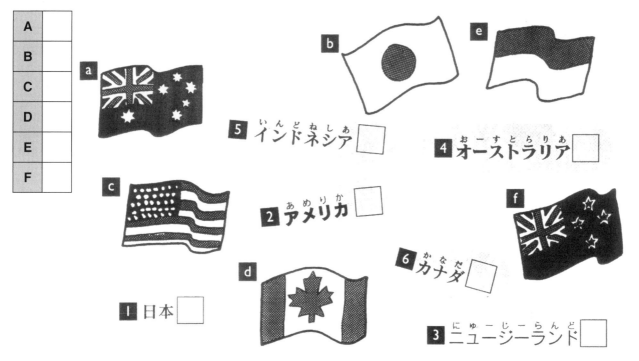

A	
B	
C	
D	
E	
F	

5 インドネシア □

4 オーストラリア □

2 アメリカ □

6 カナダ □

1 日本 □

3 ニュージーランド □

1. Listen to your teacher read out the sentences.
2. Match the student with the country they come from.
3. Introduce yourself as that student and say where you are from.

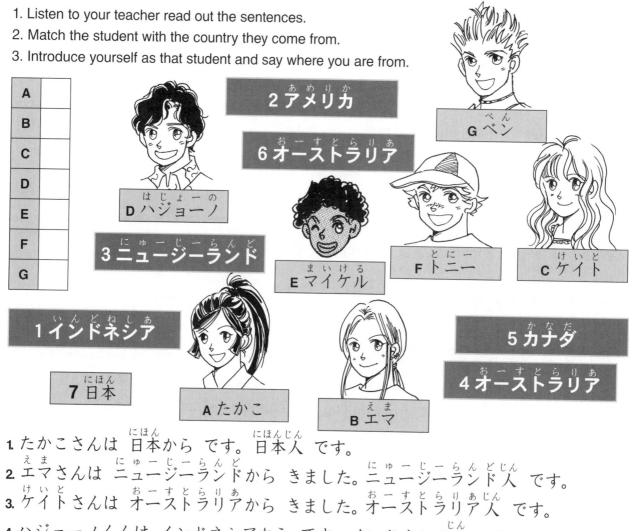

A	
B	
C	
D	
E	
F	
G	

2 アメリカ

6 オーストラリア

G ベン

D ハジョーノ

3 ニュージーランド

E マイケル

F トニー

C ケイト

1 インドネシア

5 カナダ

7 日本

4 オーストラリア

A たかこ

B エマ

1. たかこさんは 日本から です。日本人 です。
2. エマさんは ニュージーランドから きました。ニュージーランド人 です。
3. ケイトさんは オーストラリアから きました。オーストラリア人 です。
4. ハジョーノくんは インドネシアから です。インドネシア人 です。
5. マイケルさんは アメリカから です。アメリカ人 です。
6. トニーくんは カナダから きました。カナダ人 です。
7. ベンくんは オーストラリアから です。オーストラリア人 です。

Some very famous people have come to visit Nakayama Gakuen. Because they have trouble speaking Japanese you have been asked to interpret for them. Record your answer onto a tape. This is what they want to say:

A Hi everyone! I'm Cameron Diaz. I come from the USA. I am an American.
B Hello everyone! I'm Nicole Kidman. I come from Australia. I am an Australian.
C Hello everyone. I'm Russell Crowe. I come from New Zealand. I am a New Zealander.
D I'm Jim Carrey. I am from Canada. I am Canadian. I'm pleased to meet you.

10

You are an interpreter hosting an international soccer tournament in Japan. Link each team to its team banner.

オーストラリアから
きました。

アメリカから
きました。

カナダから
きました。

インドネシアから
きました。

日本から
きました。

ニュージーランド
から きました。

| America | Australia | Canada | Indonesia | Japan | New Zealand |

11

どんなあじ

二 **Asking where someone's home is and responding.**

Key Q & A

1 Listen to the items, look at the pictures and repeat.
2 Listen to the items and read along with the CD.

うちは どこ ですか。	シドニー です。
	ニューヨーク です。
	うちは オークランド です。

一

二

三

12

Listen to the どんなあじ二 はなしましょう and answer the questions in English.

1 Where is Asami's home? _____

Where is Akio's home? _____

2 Where is Harjono's home? _____

Where is Kate's home? _____

Listen to the CD and fill in the world map with the name of the person who lives in each city. The list of names is provided below.

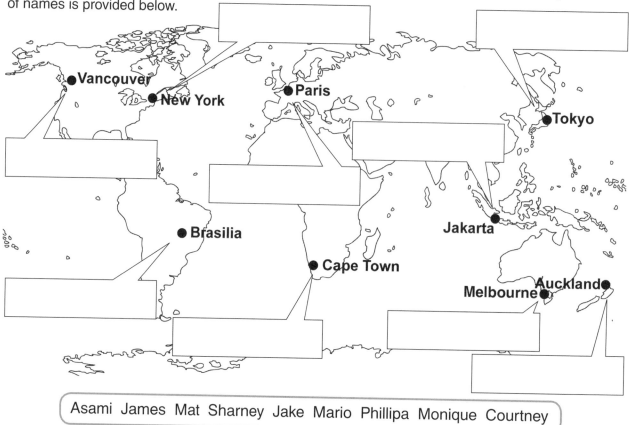

Asami James Mat Sharney Jake Mario Phillipa Monique Courtney

Can you recognise these eyes? Who do they belong to and where did their owners come from? Write down your answers, then listen to Madame X interview them to check your answers.

A

Name: _____

Country: _____

B

Name: _____

Home: _____

C

Name: _____

Country: _____

D

Name: _____

Home: _____

Your friend David is going to Japan on a two-week baseball tour. As captain of the team, he has to give a short introductory speech. Help him say the following and record the speech on tape.

'Hello everyone.
I'm David.
I'm 15 years old.
I come from Melbourne.
I'm pleased to meet you.'

Amy has won a scholarship to a Japanese school. She must introduce herself briefly at assembly. Help her with her speech by recording what she wants to say on tape.

'Hello everyone.
I'm Australian.
My home is in Sydney.
My name is Amy Gibson.
I'm 14 years old.
I'm pleased to meet you.'

16

Take turns with your partner to introduce yourself in Japanese using the information on these student ID cards.

Student Card

Name: Carrie Baker
Address: 283 Main Street Chadron
       Nebraska 69337
       USA
       987-9622
Nationality: American
Age: 13

Student Card

Name: Hasan Karini
Address: 23-29 Jalan Palmorah
       Selatan Jakarta 10276
       Indonesia
       742-6856
Nationality: Indonesian
Age: 12

Student Card

Name: Tracey Shaw
Address: 14 Aloe Crescent
       Doncaster Vic 3108
       Australia
       9523-6874
Nationality: Australian
Age: 17

Student Card

Name: Mutsuko Miyazaki
Address: 5-3-29 Sakuragaoka
       Tama-shi Tokyo 206
       Japan
       788-8531
Nationality: Japanese
Age: 16

Student Card

Name: Takuya Suzuki
Address: 9-2-5 Nishikiji
       Minomoshi Osaka 562
       Japan
       576-8825
Nationality: Japanese
Age: 14

Do you remember where all the Obento students come from? Match each student with the appropriate speech bubble.

A	
B	
C	
D	
E	
F	

5 日本人 です。
うちは とうきょう です。

c

6 ニュージーランド人 です。
うちは オークランド です。

d

b

4 オーストラリア人 です。
うちは パース です。

1 カナダ人 です。
うちは ヴァンクーバー です。

2 オーストラリア人 です。
うちは シドニー です。

f

e

3 インドネシア人 です。
うちは ジャカルタ です。

a

Read the captions underneath these pictures and write the details in English.

A
わたしは ニーナ です。
アメリカ人 です。
うちは ニューヨーク です。
十五さい です。

_____

_____

_____

B
ぼくは ケン です。
ニュージーランドの
ウエリントンから
きました。十六さい です。

_____

_____

_____

C
わたしは ますみ です。
日本人 です。うちは
ながさき です。十四さい
です。

_____

_____

_____

三 Asking where someone lives and responding.

Key Q & A

1 Listen to the items, look at the pictures and repeat.

2 Listen to the items and read along with the CD.

どこに すんでいますか。	とうきょうに すんでいます。
	ニューヨークに すんでいます。
	わたしは シドニーに すんでいます。

Listen to どんなあじ三 はなしましょう and fill in the table below.

Name of the student	The place they live

20

Nationality quiz! Test your knowledge of celebrity trivia. Write true or false for the following information. Either read the sentences or have your teacher read them out for you.

T or F

A Hugh Jackman は オーストラリアに すんでいます。

B David Beckham は カナダに すんでいます。

C Kirsten Dunst は インドネシアに すんでいます。

D Orlando Bloom は アメリカに すんでいます。

E Kylie Minogue は オーストラリアに すんでいます。

21

Make up a new identity for yourself and fill in your personal ID card.

Now, survey five people in your class to find out their imaginary details. You need to ask them these questions in Japanese:

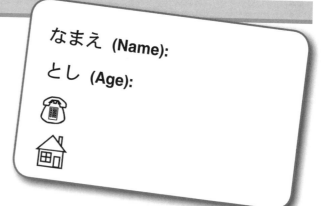

おなまえは？

なん さい ですか。

でんわばんごうは？

どこに すんでいますか。

The other students will then respond in Japanese.

Record your findings in English in the address book.

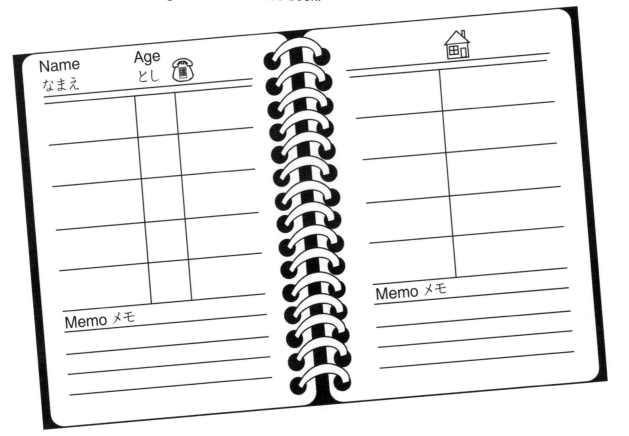

See if you can find out any further information about your friends by asking more questions in Japanese. Write this extra information in the memo space.

First, match the English sign post with the Japanese ones on the map by colouring them the same colour. Then read the sentences and write next to the sign post the name of the person who lives there.

1 わかこさんは　ひろしまに　すんでいます。
2 たけしくんは　くまもとに　すんでいます。
3 こにしきは　とうきょうに　すんでいます。
4 みるきいは　さっぽろに　すんでいます。
5 はなこさんは　ならに　すんでいます。
6 ゆみかさんは　きょうとに　すんでいます。
7 まさきくんは　まつやまに　すんでいます。
8 ゆきみさんは　あおもりに　すんでいます。

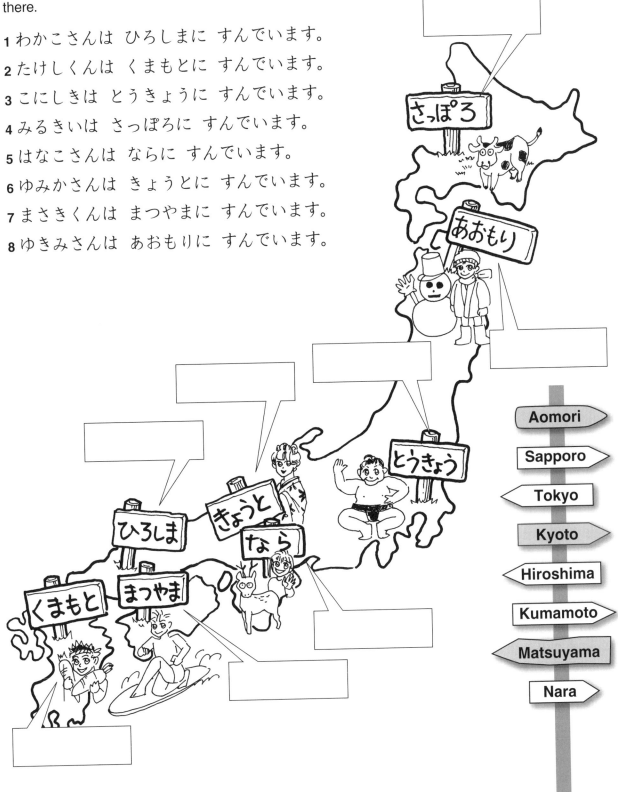

Before going to Japan each exchange student write a letter to their host family over there. Fill in the missing information using the clues at the bottom of each 'student's letter.

わたしは ＿＿＿＿ です。
＿＿ さいです。
でんわばんごうは ＿＿＿＿＿＿
です。
＿ー ス＿＿ リ＿人 です。
シドニーに ＿ ＿ ＿ います。
どうぞよろしく。

Kate
12 years old
Tel: 041355-72
Australian
Sydney

ぼくは ＿＿ー です。
＿＿ さいです。
でんわばんごうは ＿＿＿＿＿
です。
＿＿ダ人 です。
どうぞよろしく。

Tony
12 years old
Tel: 9548-1339
Canadian

わたしは ＿＿＿ です。
＿＿ さいです。
でんわばんごうは ＿＿＿＿＿
です。
＿ュージー＿＿ンド人 です。
＿ーク＿＿ンドに すんでいます。
どうぞよろしく。

Emma
11 years old
Tel: 9827-1550
New Zealander
Auckland

Now, it's your turn to write about yourself.

＿＿＿＿＿＿＿＿＿＿＿＿
＿＿＿＿＿＿＿＿＿＿＿＿
＿＿＿＿＿＿＿＿＿＿＿＿
＿＿＿＿＿＿＿＿＿＿＿＿
＿＿＿＿＿＿
＿＿＿＿＿＿
＿＿＿＿＿＿

Colour all of the squares containing hiragana in the maze. Then look for these words hidden in the maze and fill in the missing katakana.

A New Zealand   ｜ ュ ｜ ー ジ ｜ ー ｜ ｜ ン ｜ ド ｜

B Emma   ｜ ｜ マ ｜

C Indonesia   ｜ ｜ ン ｜ ド ｜ ネ ｜ シ ｜ ｜

D Australia   ｜ ｜ ー ｜ ｜ ｜ ｜ ｜

E Harjono   ｜ ｜ ジ ｜ ョ ｜ ー ｜ ノ ｜

F Ben   ｜ ｜ ン ｜

G Canada   ｜ ｜ ナ ｜ ダ ｜

H Tony   ｜ ｜ ｜ ー ｜

I USA   ｜ ｜ メ ｜ ｜

J Kate   ｜ ｜ ｜

どこから
きましたか。

<ruby>日本<rt>にほん</rt></ruby>の
こうべから
きました。

お	こ	ハ	ジ	ョ	ー	ノ	さ	ま	た
ゆ	き	な	は	い	エ	マ	た	さ	と
ニ	ュ	ー	ジ	ー	ラ	ン	ド	ち	し
け	み	せ	す	あ	お	こ	ケ	さ	ま
オ	ー	ス	ト	ラ	リ	ア	イ	た	ゆ
き	べ	な	は	い	わ	メ	ト	ニ	ー
イ	ン	ド	ネ	シ	ア	リ	な	と	ち
あ	し	け	み	せ	す	カ	ナ	ダ	あ

Colour in all the squares containing katakana in the maze. Then look for these words and phrases hidden in the maze and fill in the missing hiragana.

A Takako

B How old are you?　ん　。

C Kenichi　ん

D Telephone number　ん

E Where is your home?　ち　。

F Where do you live?　ん　。

G Where are you from?　ら　。

H Where do you come from?　。

I I am from Japan.　。

J Yuusuke

K Japanese person

L Yuki

ごちそうさま

ど	こ	か	ら	き	ま	し	た	か	う
こ	な	ん	さ	い	で	す	か	ラ	ち
か	日	ケ	ナ	ラ	ん	イ	こ	オ	は
ら	本	イ	ゆ	オ	わ	ス	ト	ラ	ど
で	か	ニ	き	イ	ば	オ	ア	イ	こ
す	ら	ア	ス	け	ん	い	ち	ト	で
か	で	カ	ア	オ	ご	ト	イ	ラ	す
エ	す	イ	オ	ゆ	う	す	け	オ	か
ラ	リ	ア	日	本	人	ケ	ハ	エ	ラ
ど	こ	に	す	ん	で	い	ま	す	か

I can:

- [ ] ask someone where he or she is from and answer when someone asks me
- [ ] say my nationality
- [ ] ask someone where their home is and answer when someone asks me
- [ ] ask someone where they live and answer when someone asks me
- [ ] say a simple self-introduction
- [ ] recognise and write the hiragana characters と、ど、う、に
- [ ] recognise and write the katakana characters オ、ス、ラ、リ、ア、イ、カ and ニ
- [ ] recognise and write the kanji characters 日、本 and 人
- [ ] recognise a map of Japan
- [ ] identify at least five interesting cities to visit in Japan.

おべんとう　クイズ

1 Circle the correct answer. (6 marks)

a どこから　きましたか means:
- how old you are
- where do you come from
- where are you from

b ぼくは　アメリカ から　きました is Japanese for:
- I come from America
- I come from Australia
- I come from Japan

c わたしは　日本人　です is Japanese for:
- I'm Indonesian
- I'm Japanese
- I'm American

d If someone asks you うちは　どこ ですか they would want to know:
- what your phone number is
- what your name is
- where you live

e わたしは　ニュージーランド人　です is Japanese for:
- I'm Australian
- I'm a New Zealander
- I'm Canadian

f If you want to ask someone where does he/she live, you will say:
- どこから　きましたか。
- どこに　すんでいますか。
- おなまえは？

2 Look at the first hiragana to identify these Japanese cities. Match each one with its English spelling by drawing lines. (4 marks)

A	とうきょう	Matsuyama
B	こうべ	Nara
C	きょうと	Tokyo
D	ひろしま	Sendai
E	さっぽろ	Kobe
F	なら	Kyoto
G	まつやま	Hiroshima
H	せんだい	Sapporo

3 Answer these questions in Japanese. (5 marks)

A おなまえは？　＿＿＿＿＿＿＿

B なんさいですか。　＿＿＿＿＿＿＿

C でんわばんごうは？　＿＿＿＿＿＿＿

D どこから　きましたか。　＿＿＿＿＿＿＿

E どこにすんでいますか。　＿＿＿＿＿＿＿

4 Who's not telling the truth? Tick true or false. (6 marks)

ケイト です。オーストラリア人 です。T / F

ハジョーノ です。日本人 です。　T / F

カーラ です。アメリカ人 です。　T / F

エマ です。カナダ人 です。　T / F

トニー です。カナダ人 です。　T / F

たかこ です。インドネシア人 です。T / F

6 Here are some Japanese words which are commonly used in English. Use the hiragana and katakana charts to work them out. (9 marks)

A からて　＿＿＿＿＿＿＿

B じゅうどう　＿＿＿＿＿＿＿

C てりやき　＿＿＿＿＿＿＿

D すし　＿＿＿＿＿＿＿

E ホンダ　＿＿＿＿＿＿＿

F トヨタ　＿＿＿＿＿＿＿

G カラオケ　＿＿＿＿＿＿＿

H スズキ　＿＿＿＿＿＿＿

I とうしば　＿＿＿＿＿＿＿

/30

かきかた

Handwritten character

Printed character

Practise writing these characters in the boxes using the correct stroke order.

1

Colour the kanji balloons the same colour as their corresponding hiragana balloon.

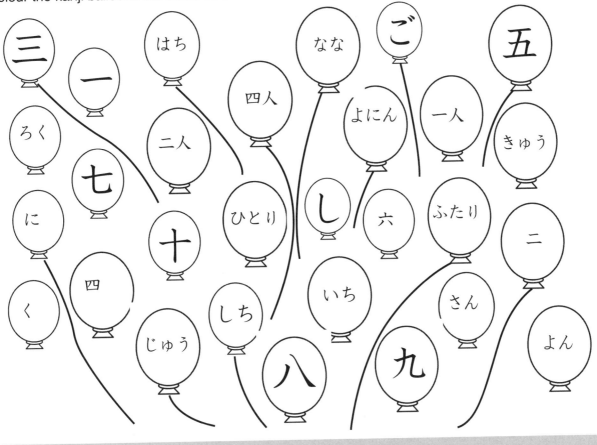

2

Find the words for all these animals in the puzzle and write them in the empty boxes.

A

B

C

D

E

F

G

H

3

Look at this picture and answer the following questions in Japanese.
Example: 三人です。

A How many of the Obento students can you see at the party?

☐☐☐☐ 。

B How many people are holding drinks?

☐☐☐☐ 。

C How many people are wearing glasses?

☐☐☐☐ 。

D How many people are wearing party hats?

☐☐☐☐☐ 。

E How many people are eating sandwiches?

☐☐☐☐ 。

F How many party guests are male?

☐☐☐☐ 。

G How many party guests are female?

☐☐☐☐ 。

H How many guests are there altogether?

☐☐☐☐☐ 。

4

一 **Asking how many people in someone's family and responding**

Key Q & A

1 Listen to the items, look at the pictures and repeat.

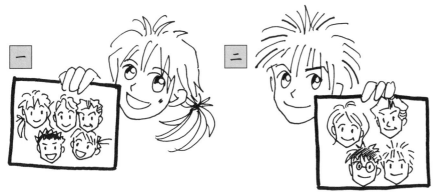

2 Listen to the items and read along with the CD.

なん人 かぞく ですか。	五人 です。
	四人 です。
	六人 です。

5

はなしましょう

Listen to はなしましょう (on p 54 of the Textbook) and practise with the person sitting each side of you by asking なん人 かぞく ですか。

6

Listen to the conversations and write the numbers in the box to show how many people each person has in their family.

a みちこ	b しんご	c ゆみか	d ごろう	e さよこ
人	人	人	人	人

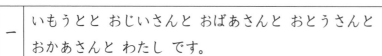

7

二 Saying who is in your family

Key Q & A

1 Listen to the items, look at the pictures and repeat.

2 Listen to the items and read along with the CD.

一	いもうとと おじいさんと おばあさんと おとうさんと おかあさんと わたし です。
二	おかあさんと おねえさんと おにいさんと わたし です。
三	おとうさんと おかあさんと いもうとと おとうとと おにいさんと おじいさんと おばあさんと ぼく です。

8

はなしましょう

Listen to はなしましょう and circle the picture of the family members as you hear them.

一 こうすけ

          (5 people)

二 まき

           (people)

あさみ

           (people)

Now, circle your family members and say how many people you have in your family and who they are.

(people)

9

Listen to the tape and write each dialogue letter next to the appropriate family picture.

1 ☐

2 ☐

3 ☐

4 ☐

10

Kyoko has been asked to introduce her family as part of a personal development assignment for school. Listen to the tape she has made and complete the table.

Family member	Name	Age
A me	Kyoko	
B		
C		
D		

Did you find out any other information about Kyoko's family?

_____

_____

_____

_____

11

Start from the centre of the puzzle and follow the kana to reveal the members of the family. Then write the full words in the boxes.

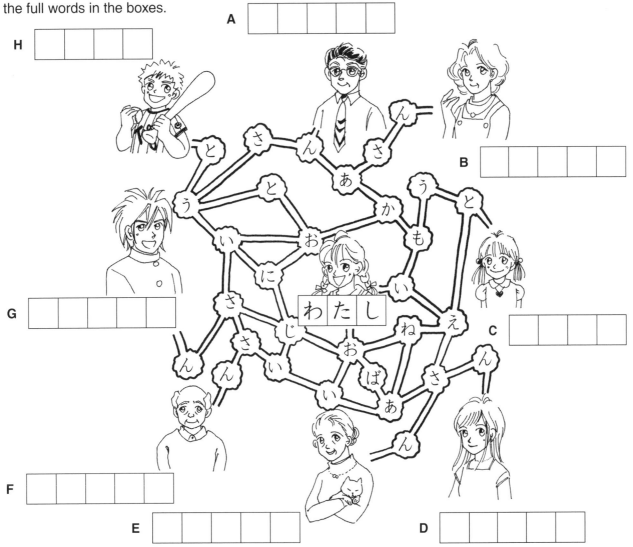

12

Identify the members of this family. Match each word with the appropriate picture.

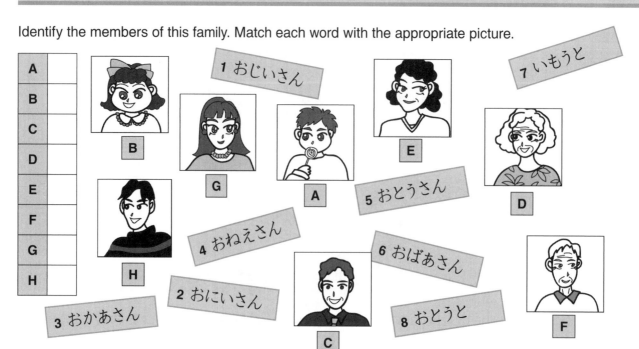

A	
B	
C	
D	
E	
F	
G	
H	

1 おじいさん
7 いもうと
5 おとうさん
4 おねえさん
6 おばあさん
2 おにいさん
8 おとうと
3 おかあさん

13

Complete the words by filling in the missing kana to reveal the members of these Obento students' families. Then, write down who is in your family.

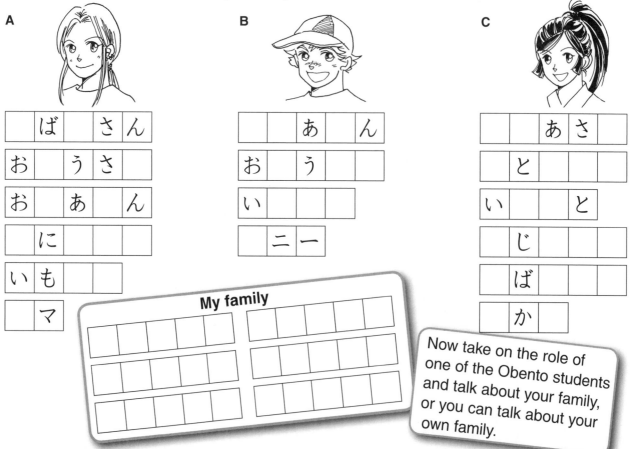

A

	ば		さ	ん
お		う	さ	
お		あ		ん
	に			
い	も			
	マ			

B

	あ		ん
お		う	
い			
	ニ	ー	

C

	あ	さ	
	と		
い		と	
	じ		
	ば		
	か		

My family

Now take on the role of one of the Obento students and talk about your family, or you can talk about your own family.

14

どんなあじ

三 **Asking what family and pets you have and responding**

Key Q & A

1 Listen to the items, look at the pictures and repeat.

2 Listen to the items and read along with the CD.

ペットが いますか。	はい、いぬが います。
	はい、ねこと うさぎが います。
	いいえ、いません。

はなしましょう

Listen to はなしましょう and answer the question.

1 What kind of pet does Akio have?

2 How about Yoshi?

Pet survey. Listen to the tape and tick the animals that each person has according to the information you hear.

	Nakamura sensei	Sanae	Yuki	Yuusuke	Tony
Dog					
Cat					
Horse					
Bird					
Goldfish					
Rabbit					

Fill in the missing kana to find out what animals they are.

A ☐ ま   C い ☐   E ☐ り   G ☐ ☐

B ☐ ☐ ぎ   D ね ☐   F ☐ ☐ ぎょ   H ☐ び

17

You have three minutes to ask, in Japanese, as many students in your class as you can about their pets. Record your findings in English below.

Question: ペット が いますか。
Possible answers: はい、います。 OR いいえ、いません。

Name	Type of pet

18

Circle the odd one out.

A いぬ ねこ うま おとうと うさぎ

B おかあさん いもうと おねえさん おばあさん おとうとさん

C おじいさん おかあさん きんぎょ いもうと おとうと

D おじいさん おとうさん おにいさん おねえさん おとうと

E じゅうにさい さんさい ごさい うるさい はっさい

F たってください すわってください へび みてください

G おにいさん せんせい おねえさん おとうと いもうと

19

Jacquie's pets are lost in the jungle. Look for the missing pets and colour them in. Also tick them off the list as you find them.

	きんぎょ
	いぬ
	うさぎ
	うま
	ねこ
	とり

20

With a partner, look at the four family pictures. One of you asks the following questions about one of the families, and the other answers. Swap roles for each familly.

A

B

C

D

なん人 かぞく ですか。
おにいさんが いますか。
ペットが いますか。

Go around your class to find students who match the information on the lotto grid. Fill in their names in English underneath the appropriate statements. Before you start, look at the statements and think about the questions you will need to ask.

Example: なん人　かぞく　ですか。

五人　かぞく　です。	おにいさんが　います。	おばあさんが　います。
いぬが　います。	おとうとが　います。	いもうとが　います。
ペットが　いません。	四人　かぞく　です。	おじいさんが　います。

22

Answer the questions in Japanese according to the picture clues.
Don't forget to include the 。and 、in your answers.

A
うさぎが　いますか。

とりが　いますか。

B
なん人　かぞく　ですか。

いもうとが　いますか。

おにいさんが　いますか。

C
なん人　かぞく　ですか。

おじいさんが　いますか。

おばあさんが　いますか。

いもうとが　いますか。

おねえさんが　いますか。

23

Look for these hidden words and phrases in the maze. Colour them in when you find them and also write them in the boxes.

A ☐☐☐

B ☐☐

C Younger brother ☐☐☐☐

D ☐☐

E Younger sister ☐☐☐

F Teacher ☐☐☐

G How many people are in your family? ☐☐☐☐☐☐☐☐☐

H Do you have a pet? ☐ ツ ☐☐☐☐☐☐

I Good morning ☐☐☐ ご ざ ☐☐☐

J ☐☐

K Mum ☐☐☐☐☐

L How old are you? ☐☐☐☐☐☐☐

M Older sister ☐☐☐☐☐

N Home ☐ ち

O ☐☐

P Snake ☐ び

Q Duck ☐☐☐

R Older brother ☐☐☐☐☐

S Grandmother ☐☐☐☐☐

T Grandfather ☐☐☐☐☐

い	な	ん	人	か	ぞ	く	で	す	か	お
も	お	ば	あ	さ	ん	う	て	き	か	と
う	は	お	に	い	さ	ん	と	あ	く	う
と	よ	う	ち	む	み	て	さ	ひ	け	と
あ	う	お	か	あ	さ	ん	つ	る	こ	や
て	ご	さ	ペ	ッ	ト	が	い	ま	す	か
き	ざ	ふ	ぎ	ち	ね	こ	つ	け	さ	な
へ	い	へ	ま	な	ん	さ	い	で	す	か
う	ま	び	か	そ	せ	ん	せ	い	こ	と
み	す	ほ	お	じ	い	さ	ん	ぬ	て	と
ち	て	お	ね	え	さ	ん	す	の	に	り

24

On a separate sheet of paper, draw or attach a picture of yourself and your family. Provide some information about yourself in Japanese, for example:

- Your name
- Your age
- Where you come from
- Your telephone number
- How many members there are in your family and who they are
- Whether you have any pets and what they are

25

おしょうゆ クイズ タイム

Circle the correct answer.

A おめでとう ございます **means:**

- Happy birthday
- Congratulations
- Thank you

B ざんねん です **is used when:**

- You're disappointed
- You're in year 3
- You're 3 years old

C いいえ、ちがいます **is used when:**

- You agree
- You disagree
- You don't know the answer

D はい、そう です。 **is used when:**

- You agree
- You disagree
- You are in pain

E When the teacher says だめ！ **you should:**

- Stop what you are doing
- Stand up
- Be quiet

F へえ？ **means:**

- I agree
- Really?
- Hey you!

ごちそうさま

I can:

- [ ] ask someone how many people are in their family
- [ ] say who is in my family
- [ ] ask someone if they have certain people in their family, for example, a grandmother
- [ ] ask someone if they have any pets
- [ ] write the hiragana characters え、く、そ、ぬ、ね、ひ、へ、も、り、る、ん
  が、ぎ、じ、ぞ
- [ ] recognise some key hiragana words
- [ ] write the katakana character ペ
- [ ] recognise some key katakana words
- [ ] identify the rooms in a Japanese house
- [ ] talk about some aspects of Japanese daily life
- [ ] use some tricks to remember a list of Japanese words

おめでとう！

おべんとう クイズ

1 Fill in the missing characters. (9 marks)

A お ＿＿ あさん   F お ＿＿ いさん

B ＿＿ とうさん   G ＿＿ もうと

C お ＿＿ えさん   H お ＿＿ うと

D おば ＿＿ さん   I ＿＿ ぞ ＿＿

E お ＿＿ いさん

2 Here are two introductions written by some students. Who are they? Write their names underneath the appropriate paragraph. Also add three other facts that you can find for each student. (8 marks)

a こんにちは。
ぼくは トニー です。
カナダ から きました。
ぼくは 十二さい です。
かぞくは 四人 です。
おとうさんと おかあさんと
いもうとと ぼく です。
ペット が います。
ねこと いぬが います。

＿＿＿＿＿＿＿＿＿＿＿＿＿＿＿＿＿＿＿＿＿＿

＿＿＿＿＿＿＿＿＿＿＿＿＿＿＿＿＿＿＿＿＿＿

＿＿＿＿＿＿＿＿＿＿＿＿＿＿＿＿＿＿＿＿＿＿

b こんにちは。
わたしは さなえ です。
日本人 です。
わたしは 十二さい です。
かぞくは 五人 です。
おとうさんと おかあさんと
おにいさんと おとうとと わたし です。
ペットは うさぎ です。

＿＿＿＿＿＿＿＿＿＿＿＿＿＿＿＿＿＿＿＿＿＿

＿＿＿＿＿＿＿＿＿＿＿＿＿＿＿＿＿＿＿＿＿＿

＿＿＿＿＿＿＿＿＿＿＿＿＿＿＿＿＿＿＿＿＿＿

3 True or false? (T /F)
ペットが いますか。 (6 marks)

A

はい、いぬと
ねこが います。

B
はい、います。
とりが います。

C

はい、うまが
います。

D
いいえ、
いません。

E

はい、ねこと
うさぎが います。

F
きんぎょが
います。

4 Match the questions and answers. (7 marks)

A エマ さん ですか。

B アメリカ人 ですか。

C うちは どこ ですか。

D なんさい ですか。

E なん人 かぞく ですか。

F どこに すんでいますか。

G ペット が いますか。

1 五人 です。

2 はい、います。とりが います。

3 いいえ。ケイト です。

4 カナダに すんでいます。

5 オーストラリア です。

6 十三さい です。

7 いいえ。カナダ人 です。

a	
b	
c	
d	
e	
f	
g	

/30

かきかた

Practise writing these characters in the boxes using the correct stroke order.

Handwritten character

Printed character

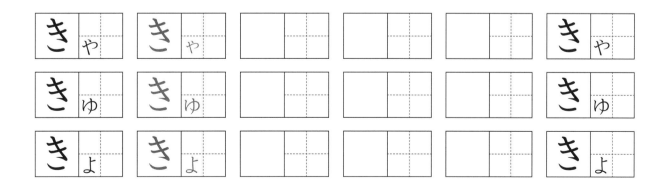

1

Circle the correct hiragana for these sounds. Practise writing the correct ones in the empty boxes. Then, read the others aloud.

A	kya	きゅ	きゃ	きょ	ひゃ	
B	sho	しゃ	にゃ	しゅ	しょ	
C	hya	ぴゃ	ひょ	ひゃ	ひゅ	
D	nyu	にゃ	ちゃ	にゅ	にょ	
E	chu	ちゅ	きゅ	ちゃ	ちょ	

2

Sort out the sounds in this bag full of words. Using different highlighers or pencils, colour in the sounds according to the key.

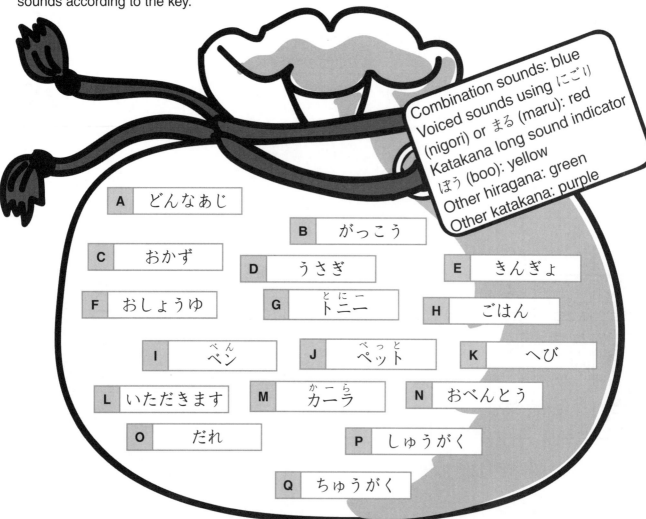

Combination sounds: blue
Voiced sounds using にごり
(nigori) or まる (maru): red
Katakana long sound indicator
ぼう (boo): yellow
Other hiragana: green
Other katakana: purple

A どんなあじ

B がっこう

C おかず

D うさぎ

E きんぎょ

F おしょうゆ

G トニー

H ごはん

I ベン

J ペット

K へび

L いただきます

M カーラ

N おべんとう

O だれ

P しゅうがく

Q ちゅうがく

3

How do these sounds change? Practise saying them aloud with a partner.

A か ⇒ が   C せ ⇒ ぜ   E ふ ⇒ ぶ

B し ⇒ じ   D と ⇒ ど   F ふ ⇒ ぷ

4

Tony has made a hiragana chart to help him remember the new kana, but unfortunately his dog walked all over it with his muddy paws. Help Tony repair the chart by completing the missing kana.

5

 **どんなあじ**

一 Asking what someone's pet is and saying its name

Key Q & A

1 Listen to the items, look at the pictures and repeat.

ガーコ

二

てんぷら
すし

2 Listen to the items and read along with the CD.

ペットは なんですか。	あひる です。なまえは ガーコ です。
	きんぎょ です。なまえは すしと てんぷらです。
	いぬ です。なまえは ポチ です。

三

ポチ

6

Listen to the information and fill in the table.

	Pet	Name
1		
2		
3		
4		
5		
6		
7		

7

Unjumble the following words and use them to label the pictures.

まう　　りと　　ひある　びへ　　さぎう　ぬい　　ぎょんき

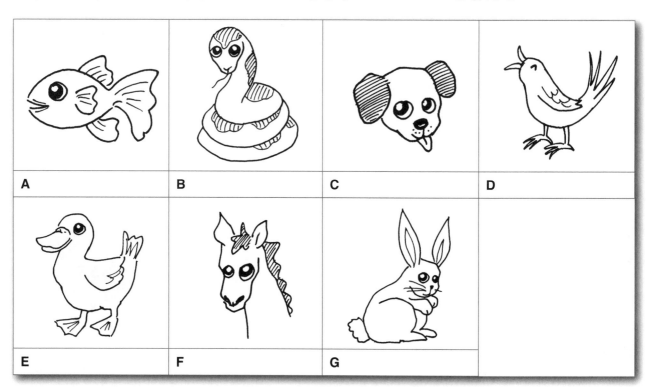

8

Nakayama Gakuen is having its annual ぶんかさい (school fete). As part of the ぶんかさい they are having a pet show. Everyone has brought along their pets to enter. Listen to the conversations at the registration desk and write down what pet each student has and to which area they have to take them to show them.

	Student name	Type of pet	Name of pet	Area number
A				
B				
C				
D				
E				

9

どんなあじ

二 Asking whose pet it is and responding

Key Q & A

1 Listen to the items, look at the pictures and repeat.

2 Listen to the items and read along with the CD.

だれの ペット ですか。	だれの いぬ ですか。
はなこさんの ペット です。	わたしの いぬ です。
だれの ペット ですか。	だれの いぬ ですか。
わたしの ペット です。	たかこさんの いぬ です。
だれの いぬ ですか。	だれの いぬ ですか。
まきさんの いぬ です。	たかこさんの いぬ です。

10

Listen to the information and fill in the table.

	1	2	3	4	5	6	7
Person	Milly	Hayden	Mallory	Matthew	Tayla	Josh	Madison
Pet							

11

After the presentation of prizes at the Nakayama Gakuen pet show, somehow all of the pets got loose. Listen as なかむら　せんせい　tries to sort out which pet belongs to which person. Draw lines to connect the pet owners with their lost pets.

a	b	c	d	e
Akira	**Masaru**	**Suzie**	**Jane**	**Kenji**

12 どんなあじ

三 Describing pets

Key Q & A

1 Listen to the items, look at the pictures and repeat.

2 Look at page 71 of the Student Book, listen to the items and read along with the CD.

一 　二 　三 　四

はなしましょう Listen and complete the table.

	Name of pet owner	Type of pet	Description of pet
1			
2			
3			
4			
5			

Then, look at page 71 of the Student book and role-play the conversations with a partner.

14

Read the sentences below. They identify some of the animals in the pet care centre. Match each sentence with the appropriate animal by writing its number in the empty box.

A わたしのペット は きんぎょ です。こわい です。

B わたしのペット は あひる です。うるさい です。

C わたしのペット は いぬ です。かわいい です。

D わたしのペット は うさぎ です。ちいさい です。

E わたしのペット は ねこ です。おおきい です。

F わたしのペット は へび です。かわいい です。

In your notebook, write similar sentences for the pets that are not mentioned.

15

Read each paragraph. Then complete the table and draw pictures to illustrate.

A わたしの ペット は いぬ です。
なまえは はな です。ちいさい です。

C おとうとの ペットの なまえは ハニー
です。あひる です。うるさい です。

B ともだちの ペット は きんぎょ です。
なまえは きん です。おおきい です。

D おねえさんの ペットは へび です。
なまえは ニーナです。こわい です。

	Pet owner	Type of pet	Name of pet	Descroption
a				
b				
c				
d				

Find out which pet belongs to which Obento student by following the grid of the あみだくじ puzzle on the next page. Start with each one of the students, for example, Kenichi. Follow the vertical line down until you reach the first horizontal line. Follow this horizontal line until you reach the next vertical line. Now follow this vertical line until you reach the next horizontal line. Continue in this way until you find out which pet belongs to Kenichi. Continue in the same way to find out the name of the pet.

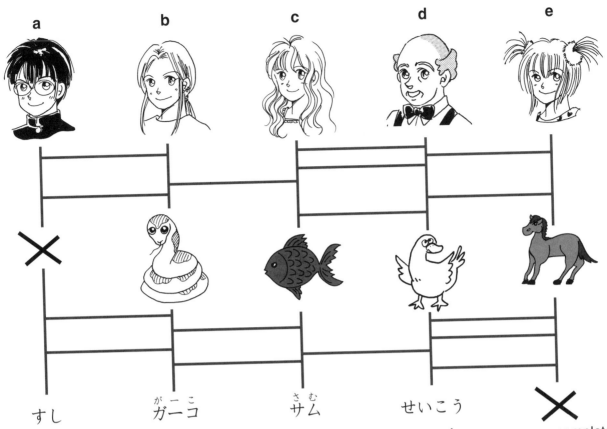

すし   ガーコ   サム   せいこう

When you have worked out which pet belongs to which person and the pet's name, you can complete the following sentences in Japanese.

A ＿＿＿＿＿ の ペットは ＿＿＿＿＿ です。 なまえは ガーコ です。

B ＿＿＿＿＿ の ペットは ＿＿＿＿＿ です。 なまえは サム です。

C ＿＿マ＿＿ の ペットは ＿＿＿＿＿ です。 なまえは ＿＿＿＿＿ です。

D ＿＿＿＿＿ の ペットは ＿＿＿＿＿ です。 なまえは ＿＿＿＿＿ です。

E ＿＿＿＿＿ は ＿＿＿＿＿ 。

Now practise saying these sentences aloud with a partner, or record them on tape.

17

Describe each picture by using the clues to fill in the blanks.

けんいち　　　　　かわいい　　　　　おおきい　　　エマ　　　ちいさい　　ゆき
ケイト　　　　なかむらせんせい　　　たかこ　　　トニー　　　こわい　　うるさい

A だれの　ペット　ですか。

＿＿＿＿＿の　ペット　です。

＿＿＿＿＿　です。

B だれの　ペット　ですか。

＿＿＿＿＿くんの　ペット　です。

＿＿＿＿＿　です。

C だれの　ペット　ですか。

＿＿＿＿＿さんの　ペット　です。

＿＿＿＿＿　です。

D だれの　ペット　ですか。

＿＿＿＿＿さんの　ペット　です。

＿＿＿＿＿　です。

18

Write three sentences under each row of pictures to describe what you see. The first row has been done for you.

けんいちくんの　ペットは　あひる　です。なまえは　ガーコ　です。かわいい　です。

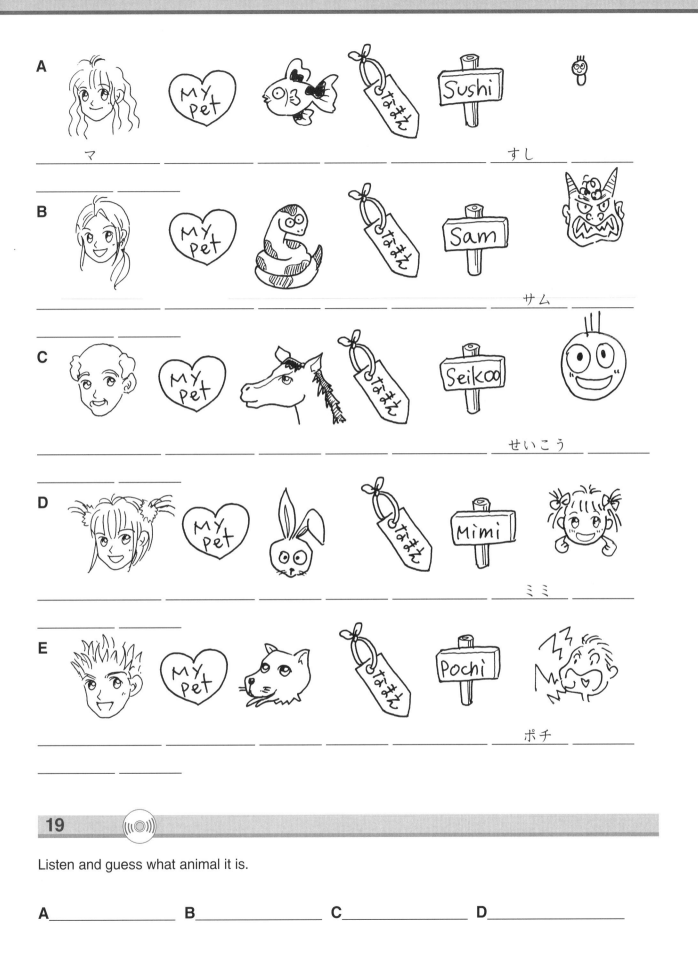

A

_____ _____ _____ _____ _____ _____
マ   すし

B

_____ _____ _____ _____ _____ _____
_____ _____   サム

C

_____ _____ _____ _____ _____ _____
_____ _____   せいこう _____

D

_____ _____ _____ _____ _____ _____
_____ _____   ミミ _____

E

_____ _____ _____ _____ _____ _____
_____ _____   ポチ
_____ _____

19

Listen and guess what animal it is.

A_____ **B**_____ **C**_____ **D**_____

四 Asking what pets eat and drink and responding

1 Listen to the items, look at the pictures and repeat.

2 Listen to the items and read along with the CD.

Key Q & A
うさぎは なにを たべますか。
やさいを たべます
うまは なにを のみますか。
みずを のみます。

21

Listen to the telephone conversations between the veterinary receptionist and three pet owners.
Complete a pet care card for each pet.

Use the following questions to survey three students in your class. Record their answers in English.

	Student 1	Student 2	Student 3
おなまえは？			
なん人 かぞく ですか。			
ペットが いますか。			
ペットは なん ですか。			
ペットの なまえは？			
ペットは なにを たべますか。			

True（ほんとう）or false（うそ）? Tick the appropriate box.

A きんぎょは あひるを たべます。　　☐ ほんとう / うそ ☐

B へびは えさを たべます。　　☐ ほんとう / うそ ☐

C とりは パンを たべます。　　☐ ほんとう / うそ ☐

D いぬは にくを たべます。　　☐ ほんとう / うそ ☐

E うさぎは おべんとうを たべます。　　☐ ほんとう / うそ ☐

F ねこは みずを のみます。　　☐ ほんとう / うそ ☐

G きんぎょは ミルクを たべます。　　☐ ほんとう / うそ ☐

ごちそうさま

I can:

☐ ask someone what pets they have and answer when someone asks me

☐ say the names of at least eight animals

☐ say a word which describes each of the pets I have learned about

☐ ask whose pet it is and answer when someone asks me about my pet

☐ ask what a particular pet eats and answer when someone asks me what my pet eats

☐ read the words for at least eight pets

☐ read the names of at least six pets

☐ read and write sentences which describe pets

☐ read and write sentences which describe what pets eat

☐ read and write sentences which say who a pet belongs to

☐ read and write all the hiragana

☐ use small や、ゆ、and よ

☐ talk about at least six things you would expect to find in a Japanese home.

おべんとう　クイズ

1 Fill in the blanks (4 marks)

A けんいちの ペット<ruby>ペット<rt>べっと</rt></ruby>は ＿＿＿＿ です。

B ＿＿＿＿の ペット<ruby><rt>べっと</rt></ruby>は きんぎょ です。

C エマ<ruby>エマ<rt>えま</rt></ruby> さんくんの ペット<ruby>ペット<rt>べっと</rt></ruby>は ＿＿＿＿ です。

D ＿＿＿＿＿＿の ペット<ruby>ペット<rt>べっと</rt></ruby>は うま です。

2 Answer the questions in English. (6 marks)

A うさぎ です。なまえは なん ですか。

＿＿＿＿＿＿＿＿＿＿＿＿＿＿＿＿＿＿

B いぬ です。なまえは なん ですか。

＿＿＿＿＿＿＿＿＿＿＿＿＿＿＿＿＿＿

C きんぎょ です。なまえは なん ですか。

＿＿＿＿＿＿＿＿＿＿＿＿＿＿＿＿＿＿

D ねこ です。なまえは なん ですか。

＿＿＿＿＿＿＿＿＿＿＿＿＿＿＿＿＿＿

E とり です。なまえは なん ですか。

＿＿＿＿＿＿＿＿＿＿＿＿＿＿＿＿＿＿

F あひる です。なまえは なん ですか。

＿＿＿＿＿＿＿＿＿＿＿＿＿＿＿＿＿＿

3 How would you ask in Japanese: (5 marks)

A Whose dog is it? ＿＿＿＿＿＿＿＿

B What is Yuki's pet? ＿＿＿＿＿＿＿＿

C What do snakes eat? ＿＿＿＿＿＿＿＿

D Whose pet is it? ＿＿＿＿＿＿＿＿

E What do cats drink? ＿＿＿＿＿＿＿＿

4 Answer the following questions. (3 marks)

A うさぎは なにを たべますか。

＿＿＿＿＿＿＿＿＿＿＿＿＿＿＿＿＿＿

B いぬは なにを たべますか。

＿＿＿＿＿＿＿＿＿＿＿＿＿＿＿＿＿＿

C あひるは なにを のみますか。

＿＿＿＿＿＿＿＿＿＿＿＿＿＿＿＿＿＿

5 Write about your pet. (2 marks)

Say you have a rabbit. Its name is Mimi. It is big and it eats vegetables.

6 Answer the following questions in Japanese. (10 marks)

A ペット<ruby>ペット<rt>べっと</rt></ruby>が いますか。

＿＿＿＿＿＿＿＿＿＿＿＿＿＿＿＿＿＿

B なまえは なん ですか。

＿＿＿＿＿＿＿＿＿＿＿＿＿＿＿＿＿＿

C ペット<ruby>ペット<rt>べっと</rt></ruby>は なにを たべますか。

＿＿＿＿＿＿＿＿＿＿＿＿＿＿＿＿＿＿

D ペット<ruby>ペット<rt>べっと</rt></ruby>は なにを のみますか。

＿＿＿＿＿＿＿＿＿＿＿＿＿＿＿＿＿＿

E ともだちの ペット<ruby>ペット<rt>べっと</rt></ruby>は なん ですか。

＿＿＿＿＿＿＿＿＿＿＿＿＿＿＿＿＿＿

/30

かきかた

Handwritten character

Printed character

Practise writing these characters in the boxes using the correct stroke order.

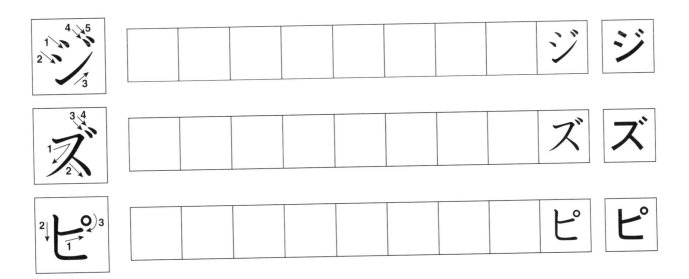

1

Fill in the missing katakana.

A ＿＿タ

B ＿＿＿＿

C ＿ー＿

D ＿＿ド＿ッ＿

E ＿＿＿＿クリーム

F ＿ー＿＿

G ＿ーンフレーク

H ＿ザ

I ＿ン＿＿＿＿＿

J ＿ルク

K ＿レー＿＿＿

L ＿ー＿＿

2

Match each word with the correct picture.

A		N		
B		O		
C		P		
D		Q		
E		R		
F		S		
G		T		
H		U		
I		V		
J		W		
K		X		
L		Y		
M		Z		

P　ごはん

R　アイスクリーム

I　サンドイッチ

A　カレーライス

K　コーンフレーク

C　ソーセージ

O　ミルク

L　チーズ

V　サラダ

U　コーラ

W　にく

H　くだもの

D　チョコレート

G　ハンバーガー

J　チキン

B　さかな

M　こうちゃ

E　おちゃ

F　オレンジ・ジュース

N　コーヒー

S　ケーキ

Y　トースト

T　たまご

X　ピザ

Z　やさい

Q　パスタ

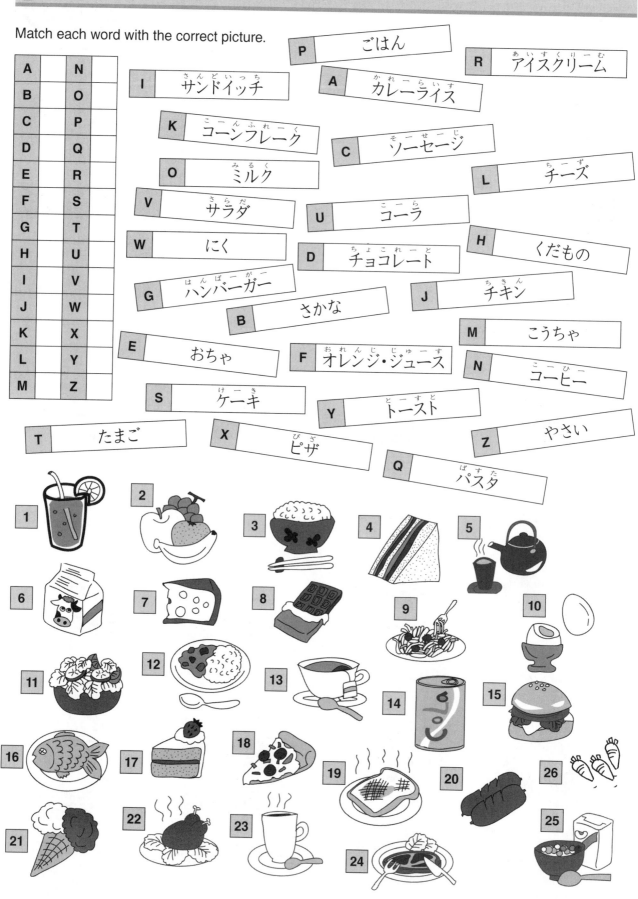

3

Find these items in the katakana puzzle and write them down.

A Two breakfast foods: _____ , _____ ,

B Nine dinner or lunch foods: _____ , _____ , _____ , _____ ,

_____ , _____ , _____ , _____ , _____

C Four drinks: _____ , _____ , _____ , _____

D Two deserts: _____ , _____

E What most Australian students have for lunch: _____ ,

F Everyone's favourite food: _____

G Which food appears twice in the puzzle? _____

H Which drink appears twice in the puzzle? _____

When you have found all of the above, rearrange the leftover letters to discover two mystery countries.

_____

_____

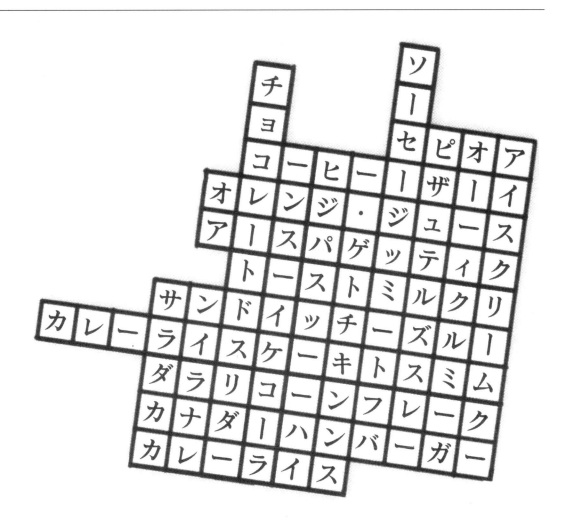

4

Circle the odd word out.

A たべません　のみません　すみません

B コーヒー　こうちゃ　サラダ　ミルク

C ピザ　ハンバーガー　ケーキ　サンドイッチ

D パスタ　トースト　コーンフレーク　たまご

E ごはん　おちゃ　カレーライス　たまご

5

 どんなあじ

一　Asking and saying what you eat and drink

1 Listen to the items, look at the pictures and repeat.

2 Listen to the items and read along with the CD.

一	あさごはんに なにを たべますか。
	コーンフレークを たべます。オレンジ ジュースを のみます。
二	ひるごはんに なにを たべますか。
	サンドイッチと くだものを たべます。コーラを のみます。
三	ばんごはんに なにを たべますか。
	ばんごはんに ごはんと おかずを たべます。こうちゃを のみます。

Listen to the どんなあじー , はなしましょう and answer the questions in English.

1 What does Yoshi eat for lunch?　_____

　What does Maki eat for lunch?　_____

2 What does Asami eat for dinner?　_____

　What does Akio eat for dinner?　_____

6

Listen to the CD and fill in the table below.

	Name of the student	Breakfast	Lunch	Dinner
A				
B				
C				

7

Go around the class and ask five people what they eat for breakfast, lunch and dinner. Record their responses.

あさごはん	ひるごはん	ばんごはん

8

Listen to the conversation between Naoko and her family outside a restaurant. Write down what everyone finally decides to have.

		To eat	To drink
A	Dad		
B	Mum		
C	Naoko		
D	Takashi		

9

Look at the survey of food eaten at each meal by these four people. In pairs, discuss the result by asking, for example, しんたろうくんは　あさごはんに　なにを　たべますか。

	しんたろうくん	あゆみ	はるか	しょうこ
あさごはん	コーンフレーク オレンジジュース バナナ	ソーセージ トースト ミルク	コーンフレーク くだもの ミルク	トースト サラダ たまご コーヒー
ひるごはん	おべんとう おちゃ	ハンバーガー コーラ くだもの	チキン サラダ こうちゃ	サンドイッチ ジュース くだもの
ばんごはん	パスタ チーズ くだもの ジュース	カレーライス ジュース アイスクリーム	ピザ コーラ チョコレート	にく サラダ ごはん おちゃ

Look at what the Obento students like to eat. Describe each meal in a Japanese sentence. The first one has been done for you.

エマ

エマさんは　ばんごはんに　チキンと　パスタを
たべます。ジュースと　コーヒーを　のみます。

18:00

A カーラ

`12:05`

カーラさんは ＿＿＿＿＿＿に
サンド＿＿ッチと ＿＿＿を ＿＿＿＿＿。
＿＿ン・＿ュー＿を ＿＿＿＿＿。

B ケイト

`18:25`

＿＿＿＿さんは ＿＿＿＿＿＿に ＿＿＿＿と
＿ダと ＿＿＿クリームを ＿＿＿＿。
＿ルクを ＿＿＿＿。

C なかむら せんせい

`07:35`

＿＿＿＿ ＿＿＿＿は ＿＿＿＿＿＿に
＿ニ＿フレーク＿ ＿＿ ＿＿＿＿＿＿
＿＿＿＿。 ＿＿＿＿＿ ＿＿＿＿。

D ハジョーノ

`19:45`

＿＿ヨーノ＿＿＿ ＿＿＿＿＿＿ ＿ザ＿
＿ダ＿ ＿＿＿＿ ＿＿＿＿。
＿＿ン＿・ジュー＿＿ ＿＿＿＿。

E すずき せんせい

`06:30`

＿＿＿ ＿＿＿＿＿＿ ＿＿＿＿＿＿
＿ニ＿フレーク＿
＿＿＿＿＿ ＿＿＿＿。ジュー＿
＿＿＿ ＿＿＿＿。

F ゆうすけ

`13:00`

＿＿＿＿＿＿ ＿＿＿＿＿
＿＿タ＿ ＿ニ＿＿ ＿＿＿＿＿
＿＿＿＿。

11 どんなあじ

二 Asking about and expressing likes and dislikes.

Key Q & A

1 Listen to the items, look at the pictures and repeat.

2 Listen to the items and read along with the CD.

パスタが すきですか。	はい、すきです。
	はい、だいすきです。
	いいえ、あんまり...。

12

はなしましょう

	あさみ	よし	あきお	まき

Listen to the conversation and write
OO if they love it
O if they like it
X if they don't

13

A little survey is conducted in class. List each food and drink in the appropriate column according to the information given.

	だいすき	すき	あんまり
A.			
B.			
C.			
D.			

14

Survey five students in your class. Ask them in Japanese if they like or dislike the food items below.
Make a graph by colouring in the appropriate sections for each response. For example:

Ask Student 1 ハンバーガー が すき ですか. If the answer is はい、すきです, colour in the first
section about the picture of the hamburger. If the answer is いいえ、あんまり, colour in the first
section below the picture, and so on.

15

Read the three letters on the next page and answer the questions.

Which of the three writers:

• is 15 years old? _____

• has a pet rabbit? _____

• has a friend called Tony? _____

• likes spaghetti? _____

• loves ice-cream? _____

• has written to Sue? _____

• likes hamburgers? _____

• wrote the letter on 16 March? _____

• mentions when her birthday is? _____

• comes from Hiroshima? _____

スーさんへ、

こんにちは。
わたしは　ゆみこです。
どうぞよろしく。
うちは　こうべです。
かぞくは　五人です。
おとうさんと　おかあさんと　いもうとと
おばあさんと　わたしです。
わたしは　おばあさんが　だいすきです。
スーさんは　なんにん　かぞくですか。
わたしは　ペットが　います。うさぎです。
なまえは　ココです。かわいいです。
ココは　くだものが　すきです。
わたしも　ココも　ひるごはんに
くだものを　たべます。
さようなら。
　　　　　　　　　　　　ゆみこより。

3月16日（水）

きょうこさんへ、
こんにちは。
わたしは　ニーナです。
アメリカから　きました。
十五さいです。
ピザと　ハンバーガーが　すきです。
アイスクリームと　チョコレートも
だいすきです。
たんじょうびは　11月24日です。
チョコレート　ケーキを　たべます。
きょうこさん、おたんじょうびは
いつですか。
てがみを　くださいね。
さようなら。

4月22日　　　　　　　　　　ニーナより。

ピーターさんへ、

こんにちは。
ぼくは　まさきです。
うちは　ひろしまです。
ちゅうがく二ねんせいです。
まいにち　ひるごはんに　おべんとうを
たべます。
チキンと　スパゲッティが　すきです。
オーストラリア人は　おべんとうを　たべますか。
ともだちの　トニーくんは　サンドイッチを
たべます。
トニーくんは　カナダ人です。
じゃ、またね。
てがみを　くださいね。
　　　　　　　　　　　　まさきより

7月30日（金）

Answer these questions in Japanese according to the picture clues.

 A あさごはんに なにを たべますか。

_____

 B なにを のみますか。

_____

 **C** ひるごはんに なにを たべますか。

_____

 D なにを のみますか。

_____

 **E** ばんごはんに なにを たべますか。

_____

 F なにを のみますか。

_____

 **G** チョコ<ruby>ちょ<rt></rt></ruby>レートアイスクリームが すき ですか。

_____

 H おちゃが すき ですか。

_____

 I パスタが すき ですか。

_____

 **J** すしが すき ですか。

_____

三 Asking and saying how often you eat or drink something.

Key Q & A

1 Listen to the items, look at the pictures and repeat.

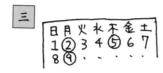

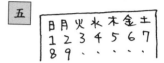

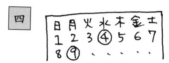

2 Listen to the items and read along with the CD.

ピザを たべますか。	はい、まいにち たべます。	ミルクを のみますか。	はい、まいにち のみます。
	はい、よく たべます。		はい、よく のみます。
	はい、ときどき たべます。		はい、ときどき のみます。
	いいえ、あまり たべません。		いいえ、あまり のみません。
	いいえ、ぜんぜん たべません。		いいえ、ぜんぜん のみません。

18

はなしましょう

Listen to どんなあじ三 はなしましょう and answer the questions in English.

1

How often does Yoshi eat a piece of cake?

_____

How about Asami?

_____

2

How often does Mr. Nakamura drink coffee?

_____

How about Akio?

_____

19

Part A

Listen to the Kidz Times Magazine interview on the CD. Place a tick next to each item that each interviewee had for breakfast. After the interviews, work out the total for each item.

		Kidz Times	Total	My class	Total
A	cornflakes				
B	toast				
C	cheese				
D	eggs				
E	sausages				
F	fruit				
G	tea				
H	coffee				
I	milk				
J	juice				
K	other				
L	no breakfast at all				

Part B

Conduct your own survey by asking ten members of your class whether they had the above for breakfast. Record the results on the table above.

さとう　さん has not been feeling so well, so he goes to see his doctor. The doctor suspects his diet is inadequate. Fill in the tables by putting a tick in the appropriate column, as you listen to their conversation.

Breakfast	every day	often	sometimes	never
Toast				
Cornflakes				
Eggs				
Cheese				
Sausage				
Fruit				
Tea				
Coffee				
Milk				
Orange juice				
Other				

Read the descriptions and match each one with the appropriate picture.

a こんにちは。ぼくは　ジムです。
あさごはんに　たまごと　ソーセージを
たべます。コーヒーを　のみます。
ひるごはんに　よく　ハンバーガーを
たべます。ときどき　ピザを　たべます。
そして、コーヒーを　のみます。まいにち、
ばんごはんに　にくを　たべます。
ときどき、カレーライスを　たべます。また、
コーヒーを　のみます。コーヒーが
だいすきです。まいにち、のみます。にくが
だいすきです。よく　ソーセージと
ハンバーガーと　カレーライスを
たべます。

b こんにちは。サリーです。
わたしは　あさごはんに　くだものと
コーンフレークを　たべます。
ジュースを　のみます。ひるごはんに
サンドイッチを　たべます。そして、
ばんごはんに　サラダと　ごはんを
たべます。わたしは　にくが
きらいです。コーヒーを　ぜんぜん
のみません。よく　おちゃを
のみます。

c こんにちは。エイミーです。
わたしは　チョコレートが　だいすき
です。あさごはんに　チョコレートと
コーンフレークを　たべます。ひるごはんに
サンドイッチと　チョコレートケーキを
たべます。そして、ばんごはんに、
にくと　チョコレートアイスクリームを
たべます。チョコレートミルクを
のみます。チョコレートが
だいすきです！！！

d こんにちは。ぼくは　あきらです。
あさごはんに、トーストを　たべます。
こうちゃを　のみます。ときどき
ごはんと　たまごを　たべます。
おちゃを　のみます。ひるごはんに、
おべんとうを　たべます。そして、
ばんごはんに、にくと　ごはんを
たべます。サラダも　よく　たべます。
まいにち　おちゃを　のみます。

A	
B	
C	
D	

1

2

3

4

Answer the following questions about yourself in Japanese.

A あさごはんに なにを たべますか。

_____

B ときどき たまごを たべますか。

_____

C なにを のみますか。

_____

D まいにち コーヒーを のみますか。

_____

E ひるごはんに おべんとうを たべますか。

_____

F ときどき ひるごはんに コーンフレークを たべますか。

_____

G ばんごはんに にくを たべますか。

_____

H なにを のみますか。

_____

I パスタが すき ですか。

_____

おしょうゆ クイズ タイム

Circle the correct answer.

A

If someone says たべてください they want you to:
- Eat
- Drink
- Leave

B

うそー！ means:
- You're right!
- You're kidding!
- Wow!

C

ひどーい！ means:
- That's great!
- That's disgusting!
- That's cute!

D

You say おいしい when something tastes:
- Horrible
- Delicious
- Sour

E

You say わたしは きらい です when:
- You hate something
- You think something is OK
- You love something

ごちそうさま

I can:
- ☐ ask someone what they have for breakfast, lunch and dinner, and answer when someone asks me
- ☐ ask someone if they like at least 10 different items of food and drink, and answer when someone asks me
- ☐ ask someone if they eat or drink at least 10 items of food and drink, and answer if someone ask me, saying how often I have them
- ☐ read and write short sentences which give information about the food and drink I have for each meal
- ☐ read and write short sentences saying which food and drink we like or dislike
- ☐ read and write short sentences saying how often we have particular food and drink
- ☐ recognise and write the katakana characters キ、コ、サ、シ、ソ、チ、ヒ、ミ、ジ、ズ and ピ
- ☐ recognise at least 15 items of food and drink which are written in katakana
- ☐ pronounce katakana words, which are borrowed from other languages
- ☐ identify at least 10 traditional and 10 non-traditional items of food and drink I could expect to find in Japan

おべんとう　クイズ

1 Circle the correct answer. (7 marks)

A If someone wanted to know what you have for breakfast they would ask:
- ひるごはんに　なにを　たべますか。
- ばんごはんに　なにを　たべますか。
- あさごはんに　なにを　たべますか。

B If you were asked なにを　のみますか。 you could answer:
- コーヒー
- ピザ
- にく

C アイスクリームを　あまり　たべません means:
- I don't like ice-cream much
- I don't eat ice-cream much
- I do eat ice-cream a lot

D If you were asked なにを　たべますか you could answer:
- ソーセージ
- オレンジ　ジュース
- ミルク

E まいにち　こうちゃを　のみます means you drink tea:
- Every day
- Often
- Sometimes
- Never

F チョコレートを　ぜんぜん　たべません means you eat chocolate:
- Every day
- Often
- Sometimes
- Never

G If you love something you could say:
- すき　です。
- だいすき　です。
- あんまり。
- きらい　です。

2 Look at the list of food and drink items. Write あ after each item if people usually have it for あさごはん , ひ for ひるごはん or ば for ばんごはん . (10 marks)

A チキン   **F** たまご
B サンドイッチ   **G** ごはん
C コーンフレーク   **H** コーラ
D ハンバーガー   **I** こうちゃ
E トースト   **J** アイスクリーム

3 Answer the following questions in Japanese. (6 marks)

A あさごはんに　なにを　たべますか。

_____

B ひるごはんに　なにを　たべますか。

_____

C ばんごはんに　なにを　たべますか。

_____

D チーズが　すき　ですか。

_____

E くだものが　すき　ですか。

_____

F ケーキが　すき　ですか。

_____

4 Match these common Japanese dishes with their English meanings by drawing a line.

A すきやき   meat and vegetables (cooked on a hot plate)

B やきとり   rice balls

C すし   beef hotpot

D てんぷら   skewered chicken

E てっぱんやき   deep-fried seafood

F おにぎり   raw fish on rice

G みそしる   Japanese miso soup

/30

いつ ですか？

かきかた

Handwritten character

Printed character

Practise writing these characters in the boxes using the correct stroke order.

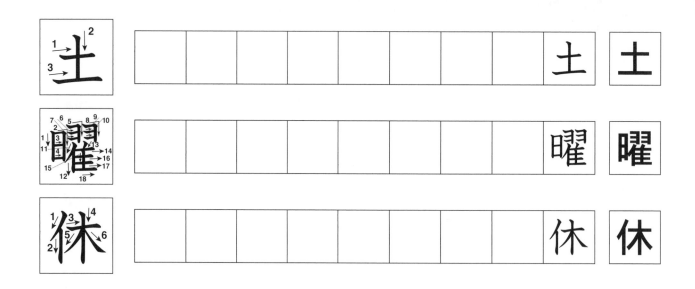

土 | | | | | | | | | 土 | 土

曜 | | | | | | | | | 曜 | 曜

休 | | | | | | | | | 休 | 休

1

Link the kanji with the corresponding hiragana.

木曜日   日曜日   土曜日

火曜日   すいようび   にちようび

きんようび   かようび

もくようび   休み 月曜日

やすみ   どようび

げつようび   金曜日   水曜日

2

Write out the following words in Japanese.

A test ⬜⬜

B camp ⬜ ヤ ⬜ プ

C dance ダ ⬜ ⬜

D party ⬜ ー ⬜ ー

E calendar ⬜ ⬜ ダ ー

F excursion ⬜ ⬜

G birthday ⬜⬜⬜⬜⬜

H time off/ holiday ⬜⬜ / ⬜⬜⬜

I swimming carnival ⬜⬜⬜⬜⬜⬜⬜⬜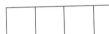

J sports carnival ⬜⬜⬜⬜⬜⬜

K today ⬜⬜

L tomorrow ⬜⬜⬜

M school ⬜⬜⬜

3

 どんなあじ

一 Asking the day and responding

Key Q & A

1 Listen to the items, look at the pictures and repeat.

2 Listen to the items and read along with the CD.

一	きょうは なん曜日 ですか。
	火曜日です。
二	キャンプは なん曜日 ですか。
	キャンプは 金曜日 です。

4

はなしましょう

Listen to どんなあじ 一 はなしましょう from Unit 7 and answer the following questions.

1 What day of the week is Akio's party?

⬜

When is Maki's party?

⬜

2 When is the test?

⬜

When is the day off (holiday)?

⬜

5

Listen to the CD and write down the day of the week being mentioned. Then draw a line to match the day with the appropriate event.

A _____   holiday

B _____   Mum's birthday

C _____   test

D _____   excursion

E _____   Pamela's party

6

Beginning at スタート (start), follow each day-of-the-week path to find out what activities the Obento students are doing on that day. Write the day in kanji near the activity.

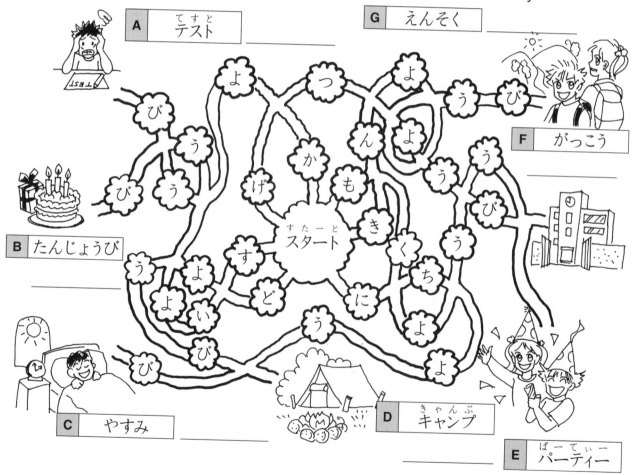

With a partner, practise asking what activity is on which day by saying
テストは　なん曜日　ですか。Have your partner answer your questions.

二 Asking the date and responding

Key Q & A

1 Listen to the items, look at the pictures and repeat.

2 Listen to the items and read along with the CD.

一	休^{やす}みは なん月 ですか。
	四月 です。
二	テスト^{てすと}は なん曜^{よう}日 ですか。
	テスト^{てすと}は 金曜^{よう}日 です。
三	たんじょうびは なん月 なん日 ですか。
	三月四日^{よっか} です。
四	たんじょうびは なん月 なん日 ですか。
	たんじょうびは 九月二十五日 です。

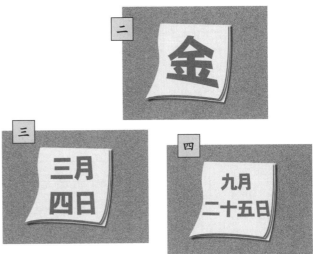

 8

はなしましょう

Listen to どんなあじ二 はなしましょう and fill in the table below.

Event	Date
School dance party	
Excursion	

 9

Listen to the items and fill in the table with the event and the date.

No.	Event	Date	No.	Event	Date
1			6		
2			7		
3			8		
4			9		
5			10		

Match the hiragana with the kanji and picture for each month of the year.

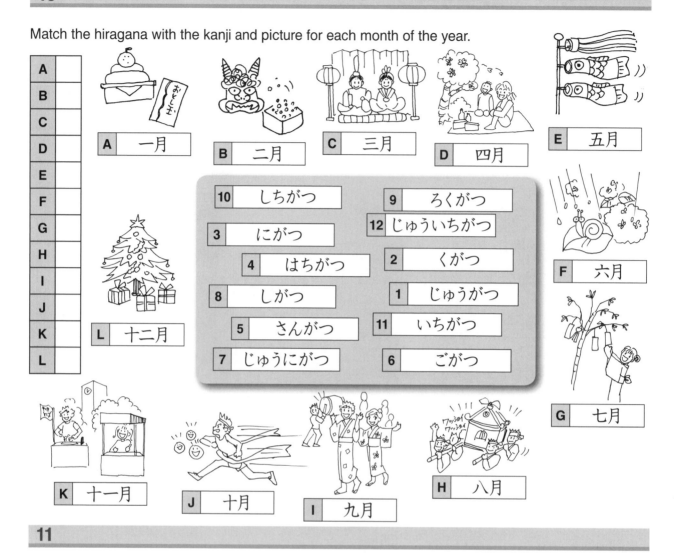

A	
B	
C	
D	
E	
F	
G	
H	
I	
J	
K	
L	

A 一月

B 二月

C 三月

D 四月

E 五月

F 六月

G 七月

H 八月

I 九月

J 十月

K 十一月

L 十二月

10	しちがつ
3	にがつ
4	はちがつ
8	しがつ
5	さんがつ
7	じゅうにがつ

9	ろくがつ
12	じゅういちがつ
2	くがつ
1	じゅうがつ
11	いちがつ
6	ごがつ

Link the kanji with the corresponding hiragana.

三日　五日　ようか

ふつか　九日　よっか　ここのか

一日

ついたち　むいか　いっか　二日　八日

十日　七日　四日　なのか

とうか　六日　みっか

Starting from the in arrow
follow the sequence of
numbers from the first of the
month to the 31ˢᵗ, drawing a
line as you go.

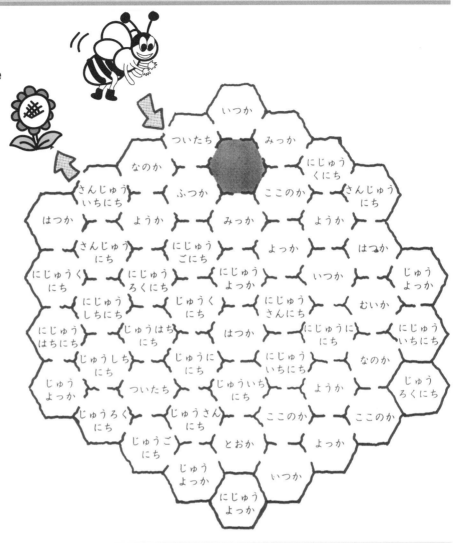

Write the appropriate kanji underneath the hiragana. (Continue on the next page.)

さんじゅうにち	むいか	にじゅうろくにち	じゅういちにち

ここのか	みっか		にじゅういちにち

じゅうよっか	とおか	さんじゅういちにち	はつか

じゅうごにち	じゅうににち	ようか	ついたち

にじゅうさんにち

じゅうろくにち

にじゅうごにち

にじゅうしちにち

よっか

にじゅうににち

ふつか

にじゅうくにち

じゅうくにち

にじゅうよっか

にじゅうはちにち

じゅうはちにち

なのか

じゅうしちにち

いつか

じゅうさんにち

14

なかむら　せんせい　has received a list of the international Obento students' birthdays, but they are all written in English. Write them out for なかむら　せんせい in kanji.

A　Emma　　24 May　　_____

B　Ben　　　13 July　　_____

C　Harjono　5 May　　　_____

D　Tony　　　21 November　_____

E　Kate　　　15 March　　_____

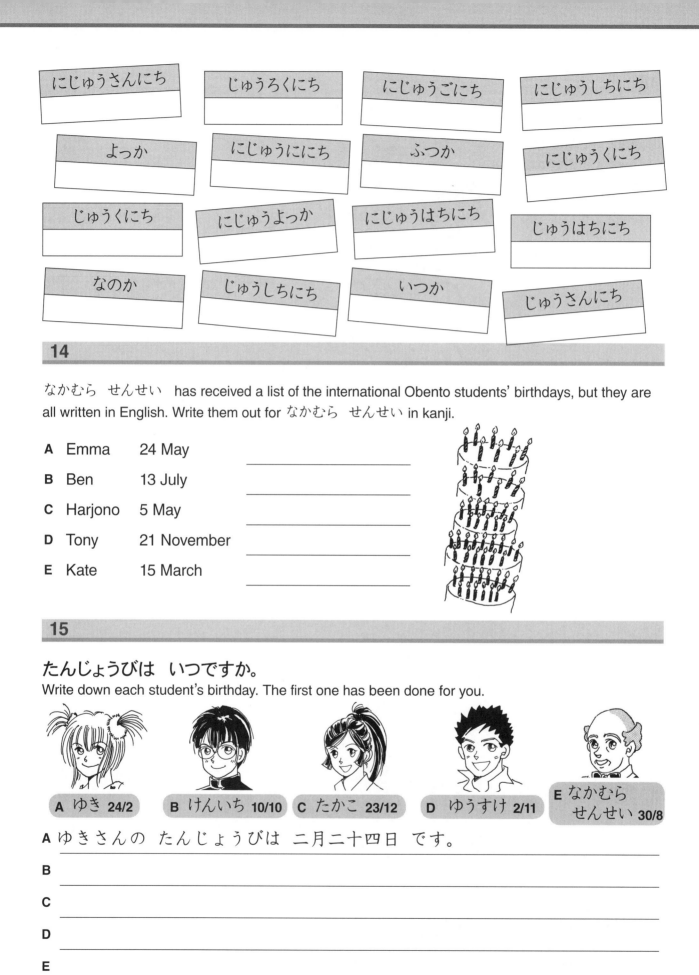

15

たんじょうびは　いつですか。

Write down each student's birthday. The first one has been done for you.

A ゆき 24/2　**B** けんいち 10/10　**C** たかこ 23/12　**D** ゆうすけ 2/11　**E** なかむら せんせい 30/8

A ゆきさんの　たんじょうびは　二月二十四日　です。

B _____

C _____

D _____

E _____

16

Work with a partner on this task. One of you asks the first question and the other finds out the answer, which both of you then write down. Swap roles for each question.

Example: 三月二十二日は　なん曜日　ですか。　水よう日　です。

A 六月六日は　なん曜日　ですか　_____

B 四月二十二日は　なん曜日　ですか　_____

C 一月十三日は　なん曜日　ですか　_____

D こどものひは　なん曜日　ですか　_____

E 十月一日は　なん曜日　ですか　_____

F 七月二十日は　なん曜日　ですか　_____

G クリスマスのひは　なん曜日　ですか　_____

H 九月十日は　なん曜日　ですか　_____

I 十一月二十九日は　なん曜日　ですか　_____

J きょう (today) は　なん曜日　ですか　_____

17

Match each picture with the correct caption. Then write the date of each birthday next to the character in figures.

A	
B	
C	
D	
E	

a

| 1 | おとうさんの　たんじょうびは　二月十六日　です。 |

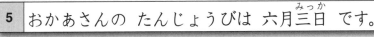

| 3 | いもうとの　たんじょうびは　八月二十五日　です。 |

c

d

b

| 5 | おかあさんの　たんじょうびは　六月三日　です。 |

| 2 | いぬの　たんじょうびは　十月三十日　です。 |

e

| 4 | おとうとの　たんじょうびは　四月一日　です。 |

18

三 Asking when something will take place and responding

Key Q & A

1 Listen to the items, look at the pictures and repeat.

2 Listen to the items and read along with the CD.

うんどうかいは いつ ですか。	火曜日 です。
	十六日 です。
	九月 です。
	あした です。

19

はなしましょう

Listen to どんなあじ三 はなしましょう and fill in the blanks.

1　The date of ＿＿＿＿＿＿＿＿＿ is ＿＿＿＿＿＿＿＿ .

2　＿＿＿＿＿＿＿＿＿'s birthday is ＿＿＿＿＿＿＿＿ .

　　＿＿＿＿＿＿＿＿＿'s birthday is ＿＿＿＿＿＿＿＿ .

　　＿＿＿＿＿＿＿＿＿'s birthday is ＿＿＿＿＿＿＿＿ .

20

A

Ask five people in your class their birthday using the question たんじょうびは　いつ　ですか。
On the survey form, fill in the names in English and the date of their birthdays in kanji.

Name	Birthday

B

Then find out the dates for the following events by asking these questions:

うんどうかいは　いつ　ですか。

すいえいたいかいは　いつ　ですか。

えんそくは　いつ　ですか。

キャンプは　いつ　ですか。

There may be other school events that you would like to include. Write down the names of the events in English and their dates in kanji.

Event	Date

21

Listen and fill in the different events that occur during the month of May on the calendar.

五月

1	2	3	4	5	6	7
8	9	10	11	12	13	14
15	16	17	18	19	20	21
22	23	24	25	26	27	28
29	30	31				

Kanji crossword

Across　Down

1 ろくがつ　　　　　　　　　　**2** げつようび

5 きんようび　　　　　　　　　**3** かようび

6 もくようび　　　　　　　　　**4** ついたち

9 にちようび　　　　　　　　　**7** にちようび

11 じゅうにがつ　　　　　　　**8** じゅういちがつ

14 ごがつじゅうはちにち　　**10** くがつ

16 さんがつなのか　　　　　　**12** はつか

17 どようび　　　　　　　　　**13** しがつようか

18 ここのか　　　　　　　　　**14** いつか

19 すいようび　　　　　　　　**15** じゅうよっか

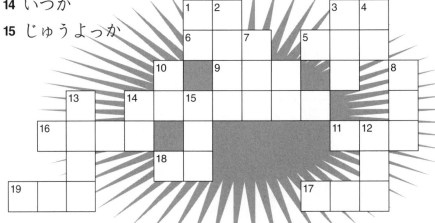

ごちそうさま

I can:
- ☐ ask what the day is
- ☐ say what the month is
- ☐ ask the date
- ☐ ask someone's birthday
- ☐ write the kanji characters 日、月、火、水、木、金、土、曜、休
- ☐ read and write the kanji for the days of the week
- ☐ read and write the kanji for the months of the year
- ☐ read and write the kanji for the dates of the month
- ☐ write the katakana characters テ、レ
- ☐ recognise some key katakana words
- ☐ read and write short sentences which give information about the date of someone's birthday, the date of a special event or celebration and the day of the week
- ☐ talk about one special event which tales place in Japan each month.

Find as many different katakana and kanji characters as possible in this puzzle and write them down in the spaces provided.

おべんとう　クイズ

1 Circle the correct answer. (10 Marks)

A If someone asked you たんじょうびは
いつ　ですか　they want to know your:
- Age
- Birthday
- Shoe size

B 12 June in Japanese is:
- 十二月六日
- 六月二十一日
- 六月十二日

C 5 August in Japanese is:
- 八月五日
- 七月五日
- 五月八日

D 二月四日　is read:
- にがつ　よんにち
- にがつ　ようか
- にがつ　よっか

E Thursday is:
- 金曜日
- 木曜日
- 月曜日

F Saturday（土曜日）is:
- The day of earth
- The day of gold
- The day of water

G If someone asked you テストは
なん曜日　ですか　they want to know:
- What month the test is
- What day of the week is the test
- What date is the test

H すいえいたいかい is:
- Sports carnival
- Wednesday
- Swimming carnival

I こどものひは :
- 五月五日です。
- 三月三日です。
- 七月七日です。

J 九月十一日（水曜日）is:
- Tuesday 11 August
- Wednesday 10 September
- Wednesday 11 September

2 Write the following in kanji: (8 marks)

A じゅうがつ　にじゅうさんにち

B いちがつ　むいか

C しがつ　ふつか

D しがつ　とおか

E ごがつ　はつか

F さんがつ　さんじゅういちにち

G くがつ　じゅうはちにち

H じゅうにがつ　ついたち

3 Answer these questions in Japanese. (5 marks)

A たんじょうびは　いつ　ですか。

B きょうは　なん曜日　ですか。

C あしたは　なん曜日　ですか。

D クリスマスの日は　いつ　ですか。

E きょうは　なん月なん日　ですか。

4 Link each Japanese festival with its correct English description. (7 marks)

A	せつぶん	Doll's day festival
B	ひなまつり	Bean throwing festival
C	こどものひ	Star festival
D	はなみ	Children's day festival
E	たなばた	Cherry blossom viewing
F	おしょうがつ	7.5.3 day
G	七五三	New Year

/30

かきかた

Handwritten character

Printed character

Practise writing these characters in the boxes using the correct stroke order.

| | | | | | | | | ロ | ロ |

| | | | | | | | | ギ | ギ |

| | | | | | | | | グ | グ |

| | | | | | | | | バ | バ |

| | | | | | | | | ボ | ボ |

| | | | | | | | | ポ | ポ |

1

Fill in the missing katakana. All of these words are connected with sports and other interests.

A コ＿ピュー＿ー

B バ＿ケット＿ー＿

C ク＿＿＿ット

D ＿ー ラーブ＿ー ド

E ソ＿＿＿ボール

F ＿ッ トボー＿

G ピア＿

H ＿ーフィン

I イ＿ド＿シ＿ご

J ラ＿ビー

2

The puzzle contains 19 hidden words for different sports, foods and drinks. Highlight all the words that you can find in the puzzle, then write them down in the appropriate spaces.

A チー＿

B ＿＿＿ク

C ＿ア＿

D チ＿＿＿

E テ＿＿＿

F ＿＿＿＿プ＿

G サ＿＿＿

H ＿ケー＿

I ＿グ＿＿

J ス＿ー＿

K ホ＿＿ー

L ＿ー＿＿ー

M ク＿＿ッ＿

N ＿ー＿

O ＿ス＿

P サーフ＿ン

Q ソ＿＿＿ボー＿

R ＿ン＿ュー＿ー

S ＿＿ー＿ーブ＿ー ド

3

Unjumble these words and rewrite them correctly.

A アピノ   _____

B スランレト   _____

C クックピニ   _____

D ラビグー   _____

E トーケス   _____

F トデーパ   _____

G ピュコターンー   _____

H スケルーボッバト   _____

I ドーレブラーロー   _____

J ボネットルー   _____

K リクトッケ   _____

L トボソールフ   _____

4

— **Asking and telling about hobbies and interests**

Key Q & A

1 Listen to the items, look at the pictures and repeat.

 一   二    三    四

2 Listen to the items and read along with the CD.

	サーフィン です。
しゅみは なん ですか。	しゅみは コンピューター です。
	わたしの しゅみは りょうり です。
	おとうさんの しゅみは りょうり です。

5

Listen to the CD and find out the hobbies of each of these people.

	Name	Hobby		Name	Hobby
A	Phillip		**D**	Sam	
B	Jean		**E**	Joshua	
C	Meera		**F**	Tiffany	

6

Answer the following question for each picture. しゅみは なん ですか。

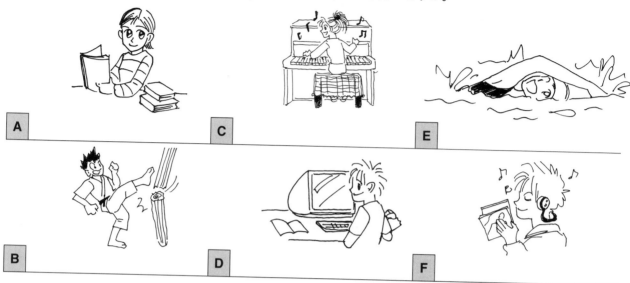

A

C

E

B

D

F

7

Conduct a survey among five students in your class to find out about their hobbies. Write each student's name at the top, then ask him/her しゅみは なん ですか。 Tick the appropriate hobbies in the table. If any of the students have a hobby that is not listed, add it to the first column.

Name	1	2	3	4	5
じょうば					
おんがく					
コンピューター					
どくしょ					
ピアノ					
りょうり					
サーフィン					
スポーツ					

二 Asking and saying what kind of sports someone plays

Key Q & A

1 Listen to the items, look at the pictures and repeat.

一 二 三 四

2 Listen to the items and read along with the CD.

どんな スポーツを しますか。	バスケットボールを します。
	わたしは じょうばを します。
	わたしも すいえいを します。
	ぼくは すいえいを します。

9

Listen to the items and fill in the table indicating what sports each person plays.

	Sport
Person 1	
Person 2	
Person 3	
Person 4	
Person 5	
Person 6	

Part A

You have received personal profiles of four Japanese exchange students. Read them and answer the questions, then choose one student whom you would like to stay with you.

Part B

In your notebook, make up your own personal profile to send to Japan.

なまえ: いとい　じゅん	とし: 十三さい
がくねん: ちゅうがく　二ねんせい	
まち: こうべ	
たんじょうび: 五月六日	

しゅみは　なんですか。
しゅみは　コンピューターと　おんがく　です。
ロックが　すきです。

どんなスポーツを　しますか。
サッカーと　からてと　けんどうを　します。

Name: _____   Sports: _____

Age: _____

Birthday: _____   Home town: _____

Hobbies: _____

なまえ: かたやま　えり	とし: 十四さい
がくねん: ちゅうがく　三ねんせい	
まち: ながさき	
たんじょうび: 十月二十三日	

しゅみは　なんですか。
どくしょと　おんがく　です。

どんなスポーツを　しますか。
バレーボールと　すいえいを　します。

Name: _____   Sports: _____

Age: _____

Birthday: _____   Home town: _____

Hobbies: _____

c

なまえ: いしの　まゆみ	**とし:** 十五さい
がくねん: こうこう　一ねんせい	
まち: とうきょう	
たんじょうび: 九月十六日	

しゅみは　なんですか。
りょうりと　ピアノ　です。

どんなスポーツを　しますか。
スケートと　ソフトボールを　します。

Name: _____   Sports: _____

Age: _____

Birthday: _____   _____

Hobbies: _____   Home town: _____

d

なまえ: ごとう　とおる	**とし:** 十三さい
がくねん: ちゅうがく　二ねんせい	
まち: おおさか	
たんじょうび: 四月二十二日	

しゅみは　なんですか。
ピアノと　ローラーブレード　です。

どんなスポーツを　しますか。
サーフィンを　します。

Name: _____   Sports: _____

Age: _____

Birthday: _____   _____

Hobbies: _____   Home town: _____

Whom would you like to have as your host brother/sister?

11

Conduct a survey among five students in your class to find out about the sports they play. Write each student's name at the top, then ask him/her どんな スポーツを しますか。 Tick the appropriate sports in the table. If any of the students play a sport that is not listed, add it to the first column.

Name	1	2	3	4	5
バスケットボール					
ラグビー					
ネットボール					
ソフトボール					
クリケット					
スケート					
ローラーブレード					
....					
....					

12

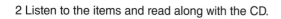

どんなあじ

三 Asking and saying if someone can do something

Key Q & A

1 Listen to the items, look at the pictures and repeat.

2 Listen to the items and read along with the CD.

	はい、できます。
	はい、すこし できます。
ローラーブレードが できますか。	いいえ、できません。
	いいえ、あまり できません
	いいえ、ぜんぜん できません。
	ローラーブレードが できます。
	ローラーブレードが できません。

13

Listen to the interviews for Kidz Times magazine on the tape and complete the table below in English.

	Hobbies/sports
Carla	
Chieko	
Yuki	
Takako	
Shingo	
Ben	

14

Here are three profiles of instructors at a local sports club. Read them and answer the questions that follow.

1

なまえ
いしだ さとる
とし 22   男 ⑳女

ぼくは たいそうと すいえいと
やきゅうと ソフトボールを
します。
そして、テニスも すこし できます。

2

なまえ
まつやま ゆみこ
とし 23   男 ⑳女

わたしは ネットボールと
バスケットボールと テニスを
します。ソフトボールと
クリケットと やきゅうも します。
すいえいも すこし できます。

3

なまえ

やまもと ゆうじ

とし 24　　　　　㊚女

ぼくは ラグビーと サッカーを
します。バレーボールも します。
バスケットボールも できます。
すいえいも できます。

A Which instructors play basketball?

_____

B Which of the three can teach swimming?

_____

C Who can teach tennis?

_____

D Which instructors can play baseball?

_____

E If you want to learn to play cricket, who can teach you?

_____

---

15 ((◎))

Listen to the interviews on the CD. Fill in the table below describing each person's preferences regarding hobbies, sports, food and music.

		Hobbies	Sports	Music	Food
A	Kenichi				
B	Harjono				
C	Kate				
D	Chieko				

16

Ask five students if they can do the following. Use the question pattern ～が　できますか。

Fill in the table with:

√ if they answer はい、できます。

X if they answer　いいえ、できません。

if they answer　はい、すこし　できます。

O if they answer　いいえ、ぜんぜん　できません。

なまえ	1	2	3	4	5
日本ご					
えいご					
フランスご					
ドイツご					
インドネシアご					
りょうり					
サーフィン					
ローラーブレード					
じょうば					

17

Here is the candidate's flyer for the class captain election. Answer the questions that follow in Japanese.

なんさい　ですか。

うちは　どこ　ですか。

しゅみは　なん　ですか。

クリケット　が　できますか。

どんな　おんがく　が　すき　ですか。

ピーター　ベイリー

十四さい　です。
うちは　アデレード　です。
しゅみは　スポーツ　です。
バスケットボールが　すき　です。
クリケット　が　できます。
ラグビーも　すこし　できます。
ポップス　ミュージックが　すき　です。

ごちそうさま

I can:

- ☐ ask someone what their hobbies or interests are and respond if someone asks me
- ☐ ask someone what sports they play and respond if someone asks me
- ☐ ask someone if they can play or do a particular activity and respond if someone asks me, saying whether I can do it, do it a little or not do it at all
- ☐ read and write short sentences which give information about hobbies, interests and sports I can play or do
- ☐ recognise words for sports and interests which are written in katakana
- ☐ write the katakana characters ク、タ、ツ、ネ、ノ、フ、ホ、ル、ロ、バ、ボ、ギ、グ and ポ
- ☐ understand basic Japanese pronunciation
- ☐ understand at least four sentence endings and what they tell me about the sentence
- ☐ understand about words that have been introduced into the Japanese language from other languages
- ☐ talk about traditional interests Japanese people might follow in their spare time.

おべんとう クイズ

1 Circle the correct answer. (6 marks)

A If someone asks you しゅみは
なん ですか they want to know:
- Your name
- Your hobbies
- Your shoe size

B If you are asked どんな スポーツを
しますか you could answer:
- ピアノ です。
- 日本ごが できます。
- すいえいを します。

C If someone asks you スケート が
できますか they want to know:
- If you can skate
- If you are going skating
- If you like skating

D If you are asked ローラーブレード が
できますか what would you answer?
- はい、できます。
- はい、すこし できます。
- いいえ、ぜんぜん できません。

E いけばな is:
- the art of flower arranging
- Japanese baseball
- singing to a music video

F さどう is:
- a Japanese traditional sport
- a musical instrument
- the art of tea ceremony

2 Fill in the blanks with an appropriate word. (5 marks)

A エマ さんの しゅみは ＿＿＿＿＿ です。

B どんな スポーツを しますか。
＿＿＿＿＿ を しますか。

C けんどうが ＿＿＿＿＿ か。
いいえ、できません。

D ローラーブレード が できますか。
はい、すこし ＿＿＿＿＿。

E わたしの しゅみは ＿＿＿＿＿ です。

3 Answer these questions in Japanese, according to the picture clues. (12 marks)

A しゅみは なん ですか。

_____

B どんな りょうりが すき ですか。

_____

C スケート が できますか。

_____

D しゅみは なん ですか。

_____

E どんな スポーツを しますか。

_____

F どんな おんがく が すき ですか。

_____

/23

Handwritten character

Printed character

かきかた

Practise writing these characters in the boxes using the correct stroke order.

1

Small ッ

Read the Japanese words aloud. Match each one with its English equivalent by drawing a line.

A	クリケット	football
B	バスケットボール	soccer
C	ペット	pet
D	サッカー	cricket
E	ホッケー	basketball
F	フットボール	hockey
G	ピクニック	Olympics
H	オリンピック	cassettes
I	カセット	picnic

2

Small ィ and ァ

Read the Japanese words aloud. Match each one with its English equivalent by drawing a line.

A	パーティー	Fanta
B	スパゲッティ	Vancouver
C	フィオーナ	surfing
D	フィリップ	party
E	ファミリー	CD
F	ヴァンクーバー	spaghetti
G	マディソン	Fiona
H	サーフィン	Phillip
I	ファンタ	Madison
J	シーディー	family

3

Write the following words in katakana.

A football

B tennis

C volleyball

D soccer

E hockey

F basketball

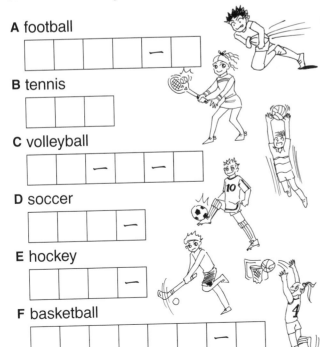

G restaurant

H department store

I concert

J picnic

K party

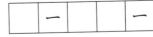

L scooter

4

Match the following Japanese words with the English word by writing its number in the box.

Weekend ☐   Beach ☐

Movie ☐   Town/city ☐

Picnic ☐   Department store ☐

Concert ☐   Friend's house ☐

Party ☐   Restaurant ☐

School ☐   Baseball match ☐

1	うみ	7	まち
2	ぴくにっく ピクニック	8	こんさーと コンサート
3	がっこう	9	しゅうまつ
4	で ぱー と デパート	10	やきゅうの しあい
5	れ す と らん レストラン	11	ともだちの うち
6	えいが	12	ぱー てぃ ー パーティー

5

(((◉))) どんなあじ

一 Asking where someone is going and responding

Key Q & A

1 Listen to the items, look at the pictures and repeat.

一 二

2 Listen to the items and read along with the CD.

三

どこに いきますか。	うみに いきます。
	えいがに いきます。
	やきゅうの しあいに いきます。

6

(((◉)))

Listen to the CD and write in English where each student is going.

A (_____)   B (_____)   C (_____)   D (_____)

E (_____)   F (_____)   G (_____)

7

Sanae is conducting a survey for her school newspaper about what people do on the weekend. Listen to the tape and complete the table below. (yes/no)

	Yuki	Kenichi	Mr Nakamura	Emma
Restaurant				
Concert				
Picnic				
Movie				
Department store				
Other? (fill in the details)				

8

ともだちの　うち　　　えいが　　　でぱーと　デパート　　　ぱーてぃー　パーティー

まち　　　こんさーと　コンサート　　　ぴくにっく　ピックニック　　　うみ

れすとらん　レストラン

Part A

The holidays are coming up. Here is a list of suggested places
to go to. Pick one place for each day and write it in your part of the diary below.

	わたし／ぼく	ともだち1	ともだち2
月			
火			
水			
木			
金			
土			
日			

Part B

What are your friends doing during the holidays? Use the pattern ～曜日に　どこに　いきますか。 to
ask two of them. Record their plans in their part of the diary above.

しゅうまつに　どこに　いきますか。 Write an appropriate sentence in each speech bubble.

10

Follow the path leading from each of the Obento students to the friend they often like to visit during the weekend. Then write down the information in a full sentence. The first one has been done as an example.

A ベンくんは けんいちくんの うちに いきます。

B _____

C _____

D _____

E _____

11

どんなあじ

二 **Asking how someone is getting there and responding**

Key Q & A

1 Listen to the items, look at the pictures and repeat.

2 Listen to the items and read along with the CD.

なんで いきますか。	バスで いきます。
	でんしゃで いきます。
	あるいて いきます。

Listen to the CD and write where each person is going and how they are getting there.

		Place	How to get there			Place	How to get there
1	ベン			6	なかむら せんせい		
2	エマ			7	エマ		
3	ゆうすけ			8	ケイト		
4	トニー			9	けんいち		
5	ハジョーノ						

13

Conduct a survey asking five people in your class how they get to school. Use the question がっこうに なんで いきますか。

	Friend	Means of transport
1		
2		
3		
4		
5		

Read the notes that the Obento students have left on the fridge for their host families. Write in English the information in the notes.

おかあさん、
あるいて ケイトの
うちに いきます。
エマ

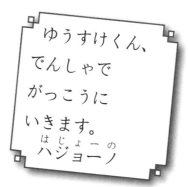

ゆうすけくん、
でんしゃで
がっこうに
いきます。
ハジョーノ

_____

_____

_____

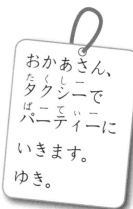

おかあさん、
タクシーで
パーティーに
いきます。
ゆき。

_____

_____

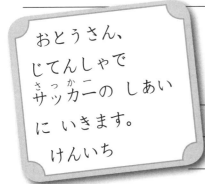

おとうさん、
じてんしゃで
サッカーの しあい
に いきます。
けんいち

_____

_____

ひこうきで
カナダに
いきます。
トニー

_____

_____

15 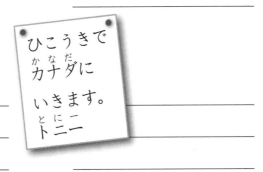 どんなあじ

三 Asking who someone is going with and responding

Key Q & A

1 Listen to the items, look at the pictures and repeat.

2 Listen to the items and read along with the CD.

だれと いきますか。	ちえこさんと いきます。
	ともだちと いきます。
	一人で いきます。

はなしましょう

Listen to どんなあじ三 はなしましょう and fill in the space to complete the sentence.

1 Yoshi is going to _____ with his _____ .

2 Maki is going to _____ with _____ .

_____ is going to _____ with _____ .

17

For this task you will need a partner and two markers (small buttons or coins). Place one marker on a picture in the first section and another marker on one of the kids below. Ask きょう、どこに いきますか for the first row and だれと いきますか for the second row. Your partner must then answer in Japanese. If s/he answers correctly, you give him/her one point. Then swap over.

一人で

四 Asking where someone is going on a particular day and responding

Key Q & A

1 Listen to the items, look at the pictures and repeat.

2 Listen to the items and read along with the CD.

一	土曜日に どこに いきますか。 えいがに いきます。 土曜日に デパートに いきます。
二	しゅうまつに どこに いきますか。 コンサートに いきます。 しゅうまつに おばあさんの うちに いきます。
三	きょう、どこに いきますか。 きょう、がっこうに いきます。 きょう、テニスの しあいに いきます。
四	あした、どこに いきますか。 あした、えんそくに いきます。 あした、ともだちの パーティーに いきます。

19

Listen to the sentences on the tape. You'll hear each sentence read twice. Piece the broken sentences on the page together by drawing links, and put them in the right order by numbering them a to e. The first one has been done for you.

金曜日に	いもうとと	パーティーに	いきます
A 日曜日に	おにいさんと	えいがに	いきます
土曜日に	ともだちと	デパートに	いきます
火曜日に	おかあさんと	ともだちの うちに	いきます
水曜日に	ひとりで	ラグビーの しあいに	いきます

Circle the most appropriate answer.

みなさん、 しゅうまつに どこに いきますか。だれと いきますか。

A

しゅうまつに パーティー_{ぱーてぃー}に いきます。
- ともだちと いきます。
- おかあさんと いきます。
- せんせいと いきます。
- そのほか ＿＿＿＿＿＿

B

しゅうまつに えいがに いきます。
- おばあさんと いきます。
- ガールフレンド_{がーるふれんど}／ボーイフレンド_{ぼーいふれんど}と いきます。
- ひとりで いきます。
- そのほか ＿＿＿＿＿＿

C

しゅうまつに うみに いきます。
- がっこうの ともだちと いきます。
- おとうさんと いきます。
- いもうとと いきます。
- そのほか ＿＿＿＿＿＿

D

しゅうまつに ピクニック_{ぴくにっく}に いきます。
- かぞくと いきます。
- いぬと いきます。
- せんせいと いきます。
- そのほか ＿＿＿＿＿＿

E

しゅうまつに デパート_{でぱーと}に いきます。
- おねえさんと いきます。
- ともだちと いきます。
- ひとりで いきます。

そのほか ＿＿＿＿＿＿

＊そのほか　other

Read these notes that were passed between classmates and answer, in English, the questions that follow.

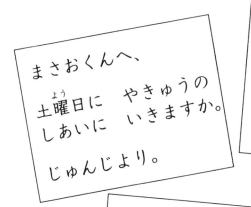

まさおくんへ、
土曜日に　やきゅうの
しあいに　いきますか。

じゅんじより。

じゅんじくんへ、

いいえ、しあいに　いきません。
おとうさんと　おじいさんの
うちに　いきます。

まさおより。

まきこさんへ、
ねー、日曜日に　けんじくんと
えいがに　いきます。そして、
ピザの　レストランに　いきます。
そして、まさみさんの　パーティーに　いきます。
すごーいね！！！

きみえより。

A What event does Junji enquire about?

_____

B Why can't Masao go to it?

_____

C Whom is Masao going with?

_____

D Why is Kimie excited? Give details.

_____

_____

Part A

Read the following sentences and find a corresponding picture for each one in the chart below.

A 木曜日に ひとりで レストランに いきます。　☐

B 水曜日に ともだちと パーティーに いきます。　☐

C 金曜日に おかあさんと うみに いきます。　☐

D 水曜日に ひとりで ともだちの うちに いきます。　☐

E 火曜日に おかあさんと レストランに いきません。　☐

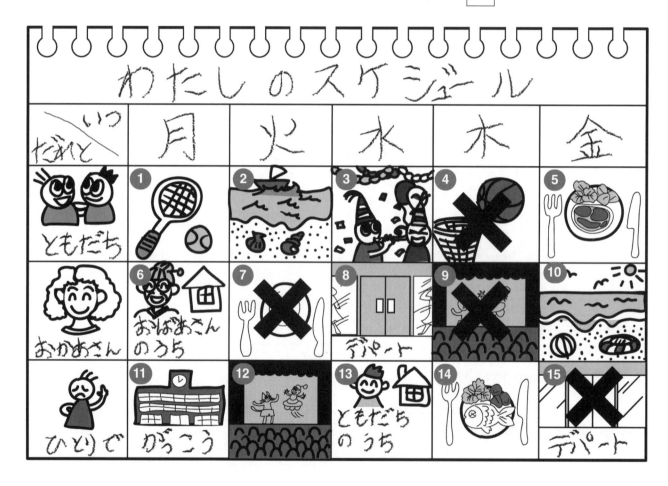

Part B

Write sentences in Japanese describing the remaining activities in the chart. Example:

1 月曜日に ともだちと テニスに いきます。

[blank lines with empty boxes]

23

What do these notes from some of the Obento students say? Rewrite their messages, in English, on the memo pads.

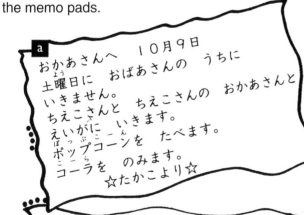

a おかあさんへ　１０月９日
土曜日に おばあさんの うちに
いきません。
ちえこさんと ちえこさんの おかあさんと
えいがに いきます。
ポップコーンを たべます。
コーラを のみます。
　　　☆たかこより☆

b ふくいせんせいへ　１１月２８日
火よう日は カーラさんの たんじょうび
です。ケイトさんと ゆきさんと
さなえさんと パーティーに いきます。
ばんごはんを たべます。
ケーキも たべます。
テニスの れんしゅうに いきません。
すみません。　エマ

Memo

Date:
To:
From:
Message:

Memo

Date:
To:
From:
Message:

しんごくんへ
きょう　日本ごの　せんせいと
日本の　レストランに　いきます。
すしを　たべます。
おちゃを　のみます。
ぼくは　すしが　だいすきです。
ピクニックに　いきません。　トニー
9月10日　またね

c

おとうさんへ　11月23日
あした　ジョンくんと　コンサートに
いきます。ジョンくんは　アメリカから
きました。がっこうの　ともだちです。
きょう　デパートに　いきます。
うみに　いきません。
ばんごはんを　たべません。
よろしく。けんいちより

d

Memo
Date:
To:
From:
Message:

Memo
Date:
To:
From:
Message:

パズル

Part A

Follow the あみだくじ puzzle to find out where the Obento students and teachers are going during their holidays and with whom. Write down your findings in Japanese sentences.

日　月　火　水　木　金　土

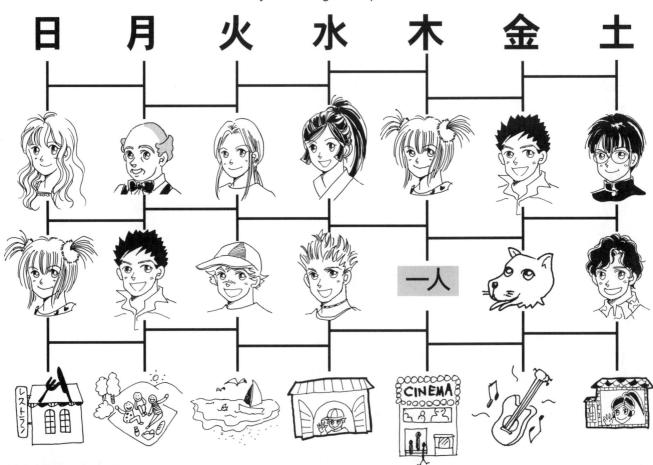

一人

A 日曜日に エマさんは ゆきさんと ピクニックに いきます。

B _____

C _____

D _____

E _____

F _____

G _____

Part B

On a separate piece of paper, make up your own puzzle. Then give it to one of your classmates to work out and tell you the answers or give them to you in writing.

ごちそうさま

I can:

☐ ask someone where they are going on a particular day

☐ ask what means of transport someone will use

☐ ask someone who they are going with

☐ read and write short sentences which give information about places I visit, when I go, how to get there and who I go with

☐ recognise words for places which are written in katakana

☐ read and write the katakana characters ウ、セ、ナ、マ、ヤ and デ

☐ talk about different activities Japanese people might do in their free time

☐ talk about particles and the clues they give about the sentence in which they are used.

おめでとう！

おべんとう　クイズ

1 Circle the correct answer. (14 marks)

A If someone asked you しゅうまつに
どこに　いきますか they want to know
where you are going on:
- Thursday
- The weekend
- Tomorrow

B If you are going to a movie you would say:
- えいがに　いきます。
- からての　しあいに　いきます。
- うみに　いきます。

C If someone asked you だれと　いきますか
they want to know:
- Where you are going
- When you are going
- Whom you are going with

D How do you say in Japanese 'I'm going to
a concert tomorrow':
- コンサートに　いきます　あした。
- あした　コンサートに　いきます。
- コンサートに　じてんしゃで　いきます。

E If you are not going somewhere, you use
the word:
- いきます
- たべません
- いきません

F Which is the most appropriate response to
パーティーに　なんで　いきますか。
- ちえこさんと　いきます。
- ちえこさんの　うちに　いきます。
- でんしゃで　いきます。

G Which is the most appropriate response
to テニスの　しあいに　いきますか。
- いいえ、テニスの　しあいに　いきません。
- おばあさんの　うちに　いきません。
- だれと　いきますか。

H だれと　サッカーの　しあいに　いきますか。
- おかあさんの　くるまで　いきます。
- ひとりで　いきます。
- レストランに　いきません。

2 Circle the odd one out. (6 marks)

A きょう　あした　うみ
B デパート　ひとりで　がっこう
C バス　くるま　かぞく
D まち　ひこうき　フェリー
E しんかんせん　タクシー　でんしゃ
F バスで　ひとりで　ともだちと

3 Answer the following questions in Japanese. (10 marks)

A しゅうまつに　どこに　いきますか。

_____

_____

B あした　がっこうに　いきますか。

_____

_____

C なんで　いきますか。

_____

_____

D だれと　がっこうに　いきますか。

_____

_____

E ときどき　おばさんの　うちに　いきますか。

_____

_____

/30

かきかた

Practise writing these characters in the boxes using the correct stroke order.

Handwritten character

Printed character

1

Takako has made a katakana chart for Kate on her computer. Unfortunately something happened during the printing and some of the characters haven't come out. Fix the chart by filling in the blanks.

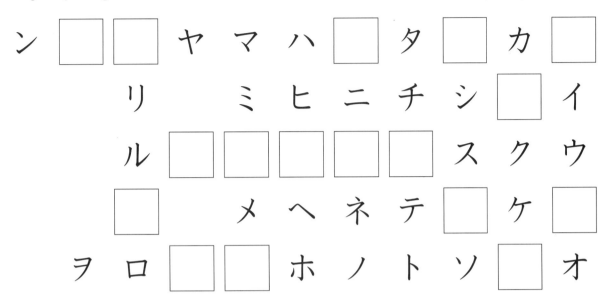

ン 　□　□　ヤ　マ　ハ　□　タ　□　カ　□

　　リ　　　ミ　ヒ　ニ　チ　シ　□　イ

　　ル　□　□　□　□　□　ス　ク　ウ

　　□　　　メ　ヘ　ネ　テ　□　ケ　□

　　ヲ　ロ　□　□　ホ　ノ　ト　ソ　□　オ

2

Find the appropriate katakana on the balloon, match the picture below and fill in the blank spaces.

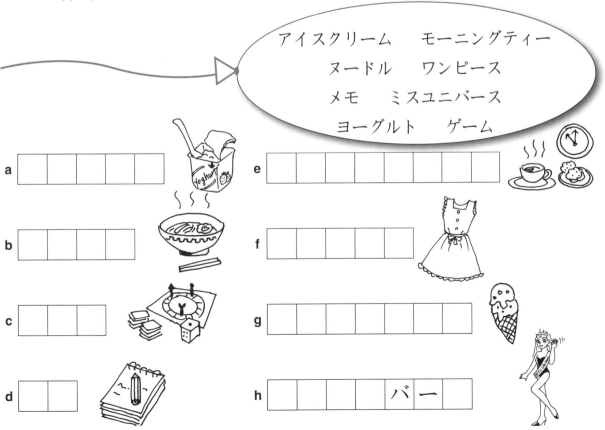

アイスクリーム　　モーニングティー
ヌードル　ワンピース
メモ　ミスユニバース
ヨーグルト　ゲーム

a ☐☐☐☐☐☐

b ☐☐☐☐

c ☐☐☐☐

d ☐☐

e ☐☐☐☐☐☐☐☐☐

f ☐☐☐☐☐

g ☐☐☐☐☐☐☐

h ☐☐☐☐ バ ー ☐

パズル

Find the words listed on the right in the puzzle and circle them.
Then write each one next to the correct picture below

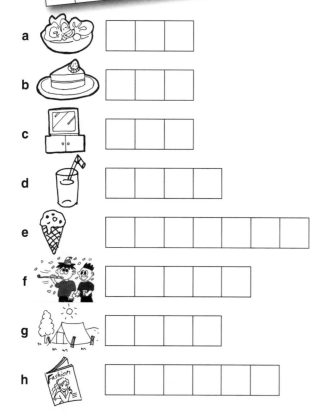

アイスクリーム	
オーストラリア	
オリンピック	
ピラミッド	
バーベキュー	
チョコレート	
パーティー	
ファッション	テニス
プレゼント	ビデオ
カラオケ	タクシー
キャンプ	Eメール
ジュース	ラジオ
ペット	テレビ
ケーキ	サラダ

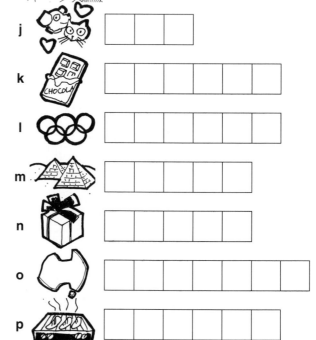

a
b
c
d
e
f
g
h

i
j
k
l
m
n
o
p

4

Write all the します words according to the picture

a ⬚⬚⬚ をします。

b ⬚⬚⬚⬚ をします

c ⬚⬚⬚⬚ をします

d ⬚⬚⬚⬚ をします

e ⬚⬚⬚⬚ をします

F ⬚⬚⬚⬚ をします

g ⬚⬚⬚⬚⬚ をします

h ⬚⬚⬚⬚ をします

5 どんなあじ

— **Asking about daily activities using** します **and** しません

Key Q&A

Write all the words according to the picture.

1 Listen to the items, look at the pictures and repeat.

2 Listen to the items and read along with the CD.

なにを　しますか。	テニスをします。
	かいものを　します。
	ホッケーの　れんしゅうを　します。
しゅくだいを　しますか。	はい、します。
	いいえ、しません。
	しゅくだいを　しません。

一　二　三　四　五　六

6

Listen to はなしましょう　どんなあじ一 and answer the questions in English.

1 What is the first speaker doing on Monday? _____

What's Akio doing on Monday? _____

2 When is the speaker doing the shopping? _____

What else is he/she doing or not doing? _____

3 What is the speaker doing today? List two. _____

The Obento kids take a vote to decide what to do in their holidays
Read their votes and match up the activity with each student by drawing lines between the text and the pictures. Note that most of the votes will be linked to 2 pictures.

Then, based on their votes decide who should hang around with whom.

friend					
friend					

どんなあじ

二 Asking about daily activities using ます and ません

Key Q&A

1 Listen to the items, look at the pictures and repeat.

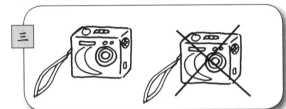

2 Listen to the items and read along with the CD.

なにを しますか。	くつを かいます。
	ざっしを よみます。
	サッカーの ビデオを みます。
なにを かいますか。	アイスクリームを かいます。
	けいたいでんわを かいます。
	本を かいます。
デジカメを かいますか。	はい、デジカメを かいます。
	いいえ、デジカメを かいません。

9

はなしましょう。

Listen to はなしましょう　どんなあじ二 and fill in the blanks to complete sentences according to what the speakers say.

1 On _____, the first speaker is going to _____ and _____.

Akio is going to _____ and _____.

2 Today, the speaker is not _____ but _____.

3 On Saturday, the speaker is not _____ but _____ with _____

and _____.

4 The speaker is _____ on _____.

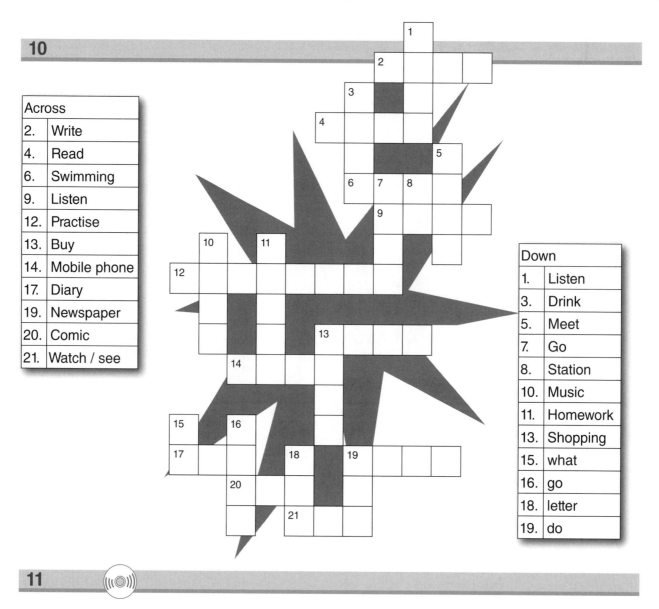

Across

2.	Write
4.	Read
6.	Swimming
9.	Listen
12.	Practise
13.	Buy
14.	Mobile phone
17.	Diary
19.	Newspaper
20.	Comic
21.	Watch / see

Down

1.	Listen
3.	Drink
5.	Meet
7.	Go
8.	Station
10.	Music
11.	Homework
13.	Shopping
15.	what
16.	go
18.	letter
19.	do

11

Listen to the items and fill in what each person is going to do.

1	
2	
3	
4	
5	
6	
7	
8	
9	
10	

Part A

Read each word on the left aloud and then draw a line to link them with the verbs associated with the words. Some verbs may have links to several words.

Part B

Write 7 sentences linking the words with an appropriate particle

For example:

コーラを　のみます。

コーラ
ラジオ
アイスクリーム
テレビ
おんがく
えいが
ざっし
てがみ
しんぶん
くつ
本
にっき
しゃしん
しゅくだい
ともだち
スポーツ
まんが
うみ
べんきょう
せんせい

たべます

のみます

ききます

みます

よみます

かきます

かいます

とります

します

あいます

いきます

ねます

_____

_____

_____

_____

_____

_____

_____

Part A

Ask 5 friends about their plans for the weekend by asking しゅうまつに　なにを　しますか。 Record their answers in Japanese.

Part B

Ask more details and record them in English. For example, your friend's answer in part A was えいがを　みます。 Now, ask なにを　みますか。 どんなえいがを　みますか。 だれと　みますか。 If your friend's answer was まちに　いきます。 ask なんで　いきますか。 だれと　いきますか。

Name	Activity	Other details だれと　なんで　どんな

どこに　いきますか。 なにを　しますか。 Write down sentences in Japanese describing the pictures.

A べんきょうを　＿＿＿＿＿　します。

B ＿＿＿＿＿

C ＿＿＿＿＿

D ＿＿＿＿＿

E ＿＿＿＿＿

F ＿＿＿＿＿

G ＿＿＿＿＿

H ＿＿＿＿＿

Listen to the items and tick the activities which the person WILL do and cross the activities the person WILL NOT do.

16

どんなあじ

Asking what other people do and are going to do

Key Q&A

1 Listen to the items, look at the pictures and repeat.

2 Listen to the items and read along with the CD.

スーリンさんは あした なにを しますか。	スーリンさんは えいがを みます。
	DVD を かいます。
	ビデオを とります。

17

はなしましょう

Listen to はなしましょう　どんなあじ三 and fill in the table below.

	Student's name	activities
一	まき	
二		

Look at the picture and write information about what each of the Obento Kids is going to do. The first one has been done for you.

1. ゆきさんは ファッションざっしを よみます。

2. _____

3. _____

4. _____

5. _____

6. _____

7. _____

8. _____

9. _____

10. _____

Kate is trying to decide what to do on the first day of her holidays. Listen as she finds out what her friends are doing and then decides what to do herself. Fill in the table with each person's plan for tomorrow.

Mallory	
Clare	
Anna	
Georgina	
Lynley	
Kate	

20

Part A

Here are three profiles. Read them and jot down notes in English for each one.

A こんにちは。ぼくは 十六さい です。
ペットは いぬ です。しゅみは スポーツ です。
ラグビーと クリケットを します。
しゅうまつに いぬと うみに いきます。
サーフィンが できます。よく、テレビを みます。
スポーツばんぐみが すき です。

ばんぐみ：program

B こんにちは。わたしは 十五さいです。
しゅみは かいものです。しゅうまつに
ともだちと デパートに いきます。よく、
ざっしを かいます。ファッションざっしを
よみます。ときどき パーティーをします。
ともだちに あいます。コーラを のみます。
チョコレートを たべます。スポーツは
あまり しません。ペットは とり です。
かわいい です。

C こんにちは。ぼくは 十五さい です。
しゅみは コンピューター です。
よく、コンピューターゲーム を します。
コンピューターで おんがくを ききます。
ラップが すき です。コンピューターで
日本ごのしゅくだいを します。ひらがなを
かきます。**E** メールを よみます。
しゅうまつに えいがを みます。
ペットは いません。

Part B

Now write your own profile
in Japanese.

21

おしょうゆ クイズ タイム

Circle the correct answer.

a When you want some one
to come here you say:
- きいて ください
- きて ください
- みて ください

b When you are late to class,
you will say:
- おそーい!
- はやく はいって
- おそくなって すみません

c When someone says
だいじょうぶよ to you, that
person is:
- Trying to reassure you
- Angry with you
- Happy for you

d If someone tells you
something and says
ひみつです。 it means:
- It is secret
- His/her name is Himitsu
- Go and tell everyone

e If you are in Japan and go
into a shop, you will be most
likely greeted with:
- おたんじょうび おめでとう
- すごいですね
- いらっしゃい

f When you want to apologise,
you should say:
- ごめんなさい
- こんにちは
- いらっしゃい

ごちそうさま

I can:
- ☐ ask about daily activities using します and しません
- ☐ ask and talk about daily activities using ます and ません
- ☐ ask what people are going to do
- ☐ link a series of activities, e.g. using そして and それから
- ☐ read and write the katakana characters ヌ, ム, メ, モ, ユ, ヨ, ワ, ヲ
- ☐ read information such as date, day or activity in a schedule
- ☐ talk about the sorts of club activities students in Japan do after school

おべんとう　クイズ

1 Write the following words in Japanese (5 marks)

magazine _____

diary _____

mobile phone _____

digital camera _____

newspaper _____

2 Change these verbs into the negative (5 marks)

いきます _____

よみます _____

ききます _____

みます _____

かいます _____

2 Complete the sentences with an appropriate verb. (10 marks)

本を_____

しゃしんを_____

おんがくを_____

テレビを_____

アイスクリームを_____

でんわを_____

ともだちに_____

てがみを_____

くつを_____

テニスのれんしゅうを_____

3 Answer the question according to the hints (10 marks)

なにをしますか。

_____

_____

_____

_____

_____

_____

_____

_____

/30

Practise writing these combination sounds.

ウィ		

シャ		

キャ		

シュ		

キュ		

ショ		

キョ		

ジャ		

ギャ		

ジュ		

ギュ		

ショ		

ギョ		

シェ		

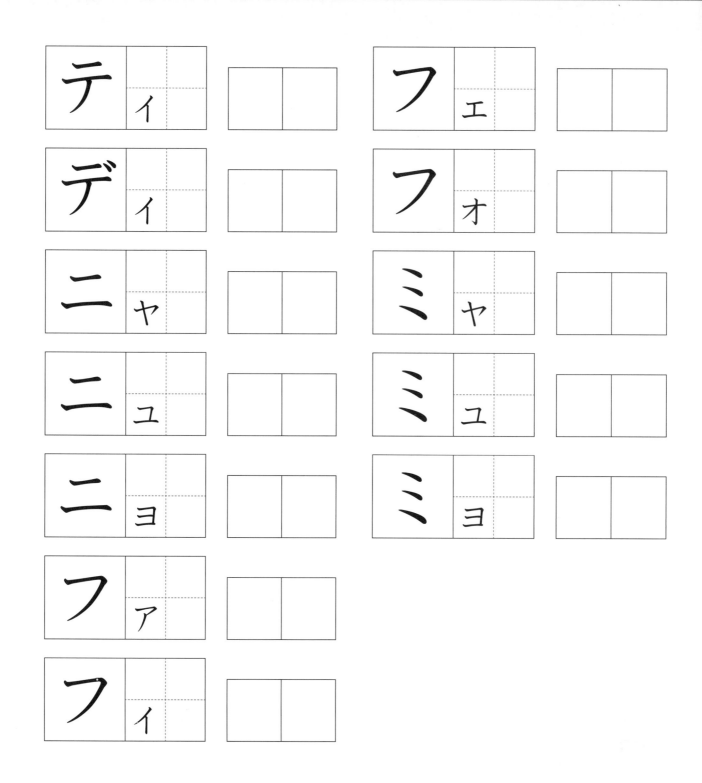

1

Circle the correct katakana. Practise writing them in the boxes.

A	**kyu**	キャ	キュ	キョ	
B	**cha**	チュ	チャ	チョ	
C	**nyo**	ニャ	ニュ	ニョ	
D	**pyu**	ピュ	ピャ	ピョ	
E	**kyo**	キュ	キャ	キョ	
F	**ja**	ジュ	ジャ	ジョ	

2

Read the words aloud, then highlight the combination sounds in the following words.

A コンピューター   **C** チョコレート

B バーベキュー   **D** ジュース

3

Draw a line between each word in katakana and its corresponding word in English.

A エミュー   party

B バーベキュー   Jakarta

C チョコレート   barbecue

D パーティー   weekend

E キャンプ   emu

F ジャカルタ   Madison

G ウイークエンド   juice

H マディソン   chocolate

I ジュース   camp

4 どんなあじ

一 Asking about free-time activities and responding

Key Q & A

Listen to the items, look at the pictures and repeat.

がっこうの あとで なにを しますか。	ざっしを よみます。
	テニスの れんしゅうを します。
	コーヒーを のみます、そして、ほんを よみます。

5

はなしましょう

Listen to the conversations one at a time and then try to act them out with a partner. The script is here to help you.

一	がっこうの まえに なにを しますか。	テレビを みます。
		しゅくだいを します。
二	ひまなときに なにを しますか。	かいものにいきます。
		おんがくを ききます。
三	金曜日のばん、なにを しますか。	ビデオを みます。
		パーティーに いきます。
四	あしたの あさ、なにを しますか。	けんどうのれんしゅうを します。
		えんそくにいきます。
五	あさ、なにを しますか。	ラジオを ききます。
六	よる、なにを しますか。	ともだちに でんわを します。

Listen to the interviews and fill in the information in English about the free-time activities of Milly, Peter and Ben.

	みリニー ミリニー	ぴーたー ピーター	そーふぃ ソーフィ
after school			
before school			
in spare time			
on Friday nights			
tomorrow morning			
in the morning			
at night			

Listen to the interview with Tomoko and write down her schedule for a typical week. If you can, write your answers in Japanese.

まいにち		
がっこうの　まえ		
がっこうの　あと	月曜日	
	火曜日	
	水曜日	
	木曜日	
	金曜日	

Listen to Kyoko interviewing her family for a personal development assignment. Write down in the table what each member of her family does in his or her spare time.

Kyoko	
Mother	
Father	
Grandmother	
Brother (Susumu)	

9

Read the questions and then circle the answers that apply to you.

A

がっこうの まえに なにを しますか。

- あさごはんを たべます。
- しゅくだいを します。
- テレビを みます。
- おんがくを ききます。
- そのほか＿＿＿＿＿

B

がっこうの あとで なにを しますか。

- スポーツを します。
- ケーキを たべます。
- しゅくだいを します。
- コンピューター ゲームを します。
- そのほか＿＿＿＿＿

C

日曜日に なにを しますか。

- テレビを みます。
- えいがに いきます。
- スポーツを します。
- うみに いきます。
- そのほか＿＿＿＿＿

D

金曜日の ばん なにを しますか。

- パーティーに いきます。
- ビデオを みます。
- ともだちの うちに いきます。
- しゅくだいを します。
- そのほか＿＿＿＿＿

E

土曜日の あさ なにを しますか。

- デパートに いきます。
- ほんを よみます。
- スポーツを します。
- しゅくだいを します。
- そのほか_____

F

ひまな ときに なにを しますか。

- ともだちに でんわを します。
- テレビを みます。
- ざっしを よみます。
- チョコレートを たべます。
- そのほか_____

10

Survey three of your friends to find out what they do in their spare time. Ask them the same questions as in the previous task. Record your findings in the table below in Japanese.

なまえ	1	2	3
がっこうの まえ			
がっこうの あとで			
日曜日に			
金曜日な ばん			
土曜日の あさ			
ひまな ときに			

11

Write down sentences in Japanese describing the pictures. The first one has been done for you.

ひまな ときに なにを しますか。

A ひまな ときに サッカーを します。

B _____

C _____

D _____

E _____

F _____

G _____

H _____

12

The sentence endings below describe free-time activities. Complete the sentences with a phrase saying when you might do each activity. The first one is done for you.

A がっこうの まえに _____ ラジオを ききます。

B _____ テレビを みます。

C _____ しゅくだいを します。

D _____ ともだちに でんわを します。

E _____ ほんを よみます。

F _____ ペンパルに てがみを かきます。

G _____ ビデオを みます。

H _____ サッカーの れんしゅうを します。

I _____ パーティーに いきます。

13

二 Suggesting and agreeing with a course of action

Key Q & A

1 Listen to the items, look at the pictures and repeat.

2 Listen to the items and read along with the CD.

一	土曜日のばん、パーティーに いきましょう。
	はい、そう しましょう。
二	あした アイスクリームを たべましょう。
	はい、いっしょに たべましょう。
三	日曜日のあさ、えいがを みましょう。
	はい、そう しましょう。
四	ひまな ときに、いっしょに コーヒーを のみましょう。
	はい、いっしょに のみましょう。

Listen to the conversation, then try to act it out with a partner. The script is here to help you.

一	あさみさん、がっこうの あとで なにを しますか。
	テニスの れんしゅうを します。
	あっ、ぼくも テニスの れんしゅうを します。いっしょに いきましょう。
	はい、そう しましょう。
	そして、れんしゅうの あとで、アイスクリームを たべましょう。
	はい、いっしょに たべましょう。
二	あきおくん、がっこうのまえにてがみを かきましょう。
	いいえ、ひるやすみに かきましょう。
	ひるやすみに？はい、そう しましょう。

15

Listen to the Japanese conversations on the tape and write down in English what each pair decides to do.

A
_____

B
_____

C
_____

D
_____

E
_____

16

Complete these sentences with an appropriate suggestion. The first one is done for you.

A　がっこうの　あとで　　えいがを　みましょう。

B　ひまな　ときに

C　水曜日の　ばん

D　あしたの　あさ

E　がっこうの　まえに

F　よる

G　日曜日の　あさ

H　あしたの　ばん

I　あとで

J　きょう

17

Present your suggestions from the previous task to people in your class. If someone agrees with your suggestion, s/he should sign in the space provided. If the person disagrees, s/he should reply using the pattern:

> いいえ、えいがは　つまらない　です。
> シーディーを　ききましょう。

18

Part A

Test your word association skills! Say each word on the left aloud and choose a word on the right that describes it. Link the words with a line. Some adjectives may have links to several words.

Part B

Look at Part A. Choose a word from the left and make a full sentence using one of the words on the right.
For example:
バスケットボールは
たのしい です。

A バスケットボール
B チョコレート
C えいが
D コンピューター
E たまご
F 日本ご
G パーティー
H コーヒー
I がっこう
J ローラーブレード
K ほん
L ピザ
M スケート
N しゅくだい
O おんがく
P おちゃ
Q テレビ
R たんじょうび
S アイスクリーム
T すいえい

たのしい

おもしろい

つまらない

おいしい

まずい

やさしい

むずかしい

A _____

B _____

C _____

D _____

E _____

F _____

G _____

19

Write down, in Japanese, three activities that you would like to do. Then survey people in your class to find out who wants to do the same things as you. You could use the pattern

いっしょに ... を しましょう。

If they have the same activity written down they should answer はい、そう しましょう。おもしろい です。 (or some other adjective)

If not, they must give a reason for refusing, for example:

いいえ、... は つまらない です。

いいえ、... は まずい です。

いいえ、... は むずかしい です。

Write the names of the matching people in the second column in Japanese, if you can. The winner is the first person to find a partner for all three activities.

	Activity	Partner's name
1		
2		
3		

20

Answer the following questions in Japanese.

A がっこうの あとで なにを しますか。

B がっこうの まえに なにを しますか。

C ひまな ときに なにを しますか。

D 土曜日の ばん なにを しますか。

E あしたの あさ なにを しますか。

F よる なにを しますか。

21

Write a suggestion based on each picture. The first one is done for you.

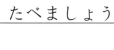アイスクリームを
たべましょう

A _____

B _____

C _____

D _____

E _____

22

Write a note to a friend.
Ask what s/he is doing on
Friday after school. Suggest
somewhere to go together
and something to do.
Don't forget to sign your
name in Japanese.,

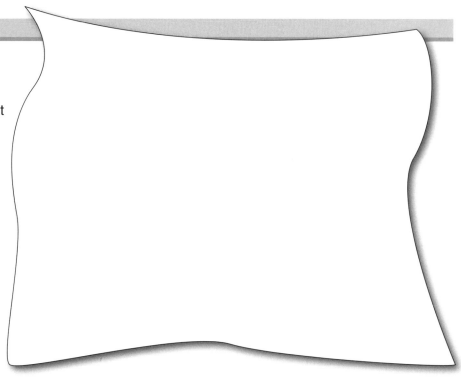

23

Read Toshio's letter to David and answer the questions that follow in English.;

デービッドくんへ

こんにちは。ぼくは わたなべとしお です。十四さい です。日本人 です。
うちは よこはま です。ぼくは ちゅうがく 二ねんせい です。かぞくは
四人 です。おかあさんと おとうさんと いもうとと ぼく です。いもうとの
なまえは さちこ です。さちこは しょうがく 六ねんせい です。
デービッドくんは なん人 かぞく ですか。ぼくの しゅみは サッカー です。
まいにち、がっこうの あとで サッカーの れんしゅうを します。
サッカーの しあいは 土曜日 です。ぼくは サッカーが だいすき です。
テレビで サッカーの しあいを みます。金曜日の ばんが だいすき です。
日曜日に いっしょに サッカーを しましょう。デービッドくんの しゅみは
なん ですか。スポーツを しますか。がっこうの あとで なにを しますか。
じゃ、デービッドくん、てがみを くださいね。ぼくも また かきます。

としお より

十月 二十三日 （水曜日）

A   How old is Toshio?

B   What year is he in at school?

C   How many are in his family?

D   What is his sister's name?

E   What year is she in at school?

F   What is Toshio's favourite pastime?

G   When does he practise?

H   When are the games held?

I   What does he suggest doing on Sunday?

J   What three questions does Toshio ask?

24

Imagine you are David. Write back to Toshio
using his letter as a guide.

---

25 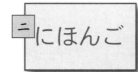 どんなあじ

三 Expressing opinions and responding to opinions

Key Q & A

1 Listen to the items, look at the pictures and repeat.

2 Listen to the items and read along with the CD.

一	アイスクリームは おいしい ですね。
	はい、おいしい です。
二	日本ごは たのしい ですね。
	はい、たのしい です。
三	しゅくだいは むずかしい ですね。
	いいえ、やさしい ですよ。
四	ビデオは おもしろい ですね。
	いいえ、つまらない ですよ。

二  にほんご

はなしましょう

Listen to the conversations one at a time and try to role-play them with a partner. The script is here to help you.

一	えいがは おもしろい ですね。
	はい、おもしろい です。いっしょに みましょう。
	はい、そうしましょう。
二	まきさん、アイスコーヒーは おいしい ですね。いっしょに、のみましょう。
	いいえ、コーヒーは まずい ですよ。わたしは コーラを のみます。
三	よしくん、ひまな ときに なにを しますか。
	カラオケを します。
	へー、カラオケ？カラオケは たのしい ですね。
	はい、たのしい です。土曜日の ばん、いっしょに しましょう。
	はい、そうしましょう。

Listen to the conversations on the tape and write down in English what each person is talking about. Also write down any responses you hear.

	Topic	Response
A		
B		
C		
D		
E		

Part A

Find out as much information as you can from these invitations, for example when each party will be held, what kind of party it is and where it will take place. Write the information in English next to the invitation.

_____

_____

_____

_____

_____

_____

_____

_____

_____

_____

_____

_____

_____

Part B

Design a notice for your school fete or for a party. Use the invitations in Part A as guide.

おべんとう　クイズ

1　Link the Japanese with its English translation by colouring the boxes the same colour. (10 marks)

あとで

Later

ひまな　ときに

ひるやすみに

あしたの　あさ

In your spare time

金曜日の　ばん

Tomorrow morning

After school

At night

がっこうの　まえに

Before school

あさ

In the morning

Tomorrow evening

あしたの　ばん

がっこうの　あとで

Friday night

よる

At lunchtime

2　How do you suggest: (6 marks)

A eating ice-cream

_____

B reading a magazine

_____

C writing a diary

_____

D going to a karaoke party

_____

E If they agreed, they could say:
- はい、そう　しましょう。
- はい、いっしょに　ききましょう。
- いいえ、だめ！

Circle all possible answers.

3　Fill in the blanks with an adjective. (5 marks)

A おかしは ＿＿＿＿＿ ですね。

B からては ＿＿＿＿＿ ですね。

C 日本ごは ＿＿＿＿＿ ですね。

D サーフィンの　ざっしは ＿＿＿＿＿ ですね。

E がっこうは ＿＿＿＿＿ ですね。

4　Answer the questions truthfully in Japanese. (5 marks)

A ひまな　ときに　なにを　しますか。

_____

B がっこうの　まえに　なにを　しますか。

_____

C 土曜日の　ばん　なにを　します。

_____

D ひるやすみに　なにを　しますか。

_____

E あしたの　あさ　なにを　しますか。

_____

5　Write down the opposites of these words. (4 marks)

A おもしろい

_____

B まずい

_____

C やさしい

_____

D やすい

_____

ごちそうさま

I can:

- ☐ ask someone what they do in their spare time and respond when someone asks me
- ☐ suggest and agree with a course of action
- ☐ express opinions
- ☐ agree and disagree with other people's opinions
- ☐ recognise words for spare-time interests which are written in katakana
- ☐ read and write short sentences which give information about spare-time interests
- ☐ read and write short sentences suggesting things to do and commenting on what these things would be like
- ☐ write all of the katakana characters
- ☐ know all the katakana sound changes including フィ、ティ、ディ and ウィ
- ☐ write words with different combination sounds in them
- ☐ prepare a short piece of Japanese writing about myself and my interests
- ☐ talk about popular digital equipment and electronic gadgets used by people in Japan.

1

Write the following new words.

A library

B trip

C temple

D souvenir

E composition

F exam

G ride/take transport

H take pictures

2

Complete this reference table with the present positive form（… ます）, past positive form（… ました）, and suggestion form（… ましょう）. Add any other verbs you know in the remaining spaces.

Present tense (will do)	Past tense (did)	(let's)	English meaning
かきます	かきました		write
		よみましょう	
みます			
	たべました	たべましょう	
		いきましょう	
かいます			
		のみましょう	
	ききました		
	しました		
のります		のりましょう	
あいます			
	とりました		
ねます			

3

一 Asking what someone did at a certain time

Key Q & A

1 Listen to the items, look at the pictures and repeat.

  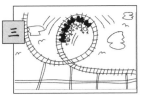 

2 Listen to the items and read along with the CD.

日曜日に なにを しましたか。	うみに いきました。
	ともだちに あいました。
	ローラーコースターに のりました。
	デパートに いきました。そして、くつを かいました。
	しゅくだいを しました。そして、テレビを みました。

4

はなしましょう

Listen to どんなあじ一 はなしましょう and answer the questions in English.

1 What did Akio do on Friday night? _____

How about Maki? _____

2 What did Asami do on the weekend? _____

Did Yoshi go to the beach? _____

5

In the table below, write down in Japanese three things that you did on the weekend.

1		
2		
3		

Then, ask 10 friends what they did on the weekend by asking しゅうまつに なにを しましたか。

If you find someone who did the same as you, write his or her name in the box.

Here is a picture taken of the Obento students on an excursion to the zoo. In the space next to each person in the picture, write the number of the sentence written about them. Also, write T if the sentence is correct, or F if it is false.

1 ハジョーノくんは バスに のりません でした。 ————

2 トニーくんは バナナを たべません でした。 ————

3 せんせいは でんわを しました。 ————

4 たかこさんは ビデオを みました。 ————

5 ゆきさんは おいしい ミルクを のみません でした。 ————

6 ケイトさんは ペットのほんを よみました。 ————

7 けんいちくんは にっきを かきました。 ————

8 エマさんは からてを しました。 ————

9 ゆうすけくんは ローラーブレードを しました。 ————

10 ベンくんは レストランに いきません でした。 ————

7

Listen to the CD and fill in the table in English. The teacher will play the CD three times for you. The dots represent the number of activities he/she did.

	When?	What he/she did.	
A	yesterday	• Went to a Japanese restaurant • Ate sushi	
		•	•
B		•	•
		•	•
C		•	•
		•	•
D		•	•
		•	•
E		•	•
		•	•

8

Change these sentences from the present tense (what you do) to the past tense (what you did).

A りょこうに いきます。

B コーラを のみます。
   こ ー ら

C おみやげを かいます。

D チョコレート ケーキを たべます。
   ちょ こ れ ー と け ー き

E カセットを ききます。
   か せ っ と

F ともだちに あいます。

G でんしゃに のります。

H なにを しますか。

I じてんしゃで いきます。

J てがみを かきます。

Answer these questions truthfully in Japanese, as shown in the example.

Question:　　きのう、テレビを　みましたか。

Answer:　　　はい、テレビを　みました。

Or:　　いいえ、みません　でした。ビデオを　みました。

A きのう、くつを　かいましたか。

_____

B しゅうまつに　アイスクリームを　たべましたか。

_____

C 十二月に　うみに　いきましたか。

_____

D 金曜日に　しゅくだいを　しましたか。

_____

E あさごはんに　トーストを　たべましたか。

_____

F きょう、じてんしゃに　のりましたか。

_____

10 ((( ))) どんなあじ

二　Asking how something is like and responding

Key Q & A

1 Listen to the items, look at the pictures and repeat.

2 Listen to the items and read along with the CD.

一	しけんは　どう　でしたか。	むずかしかった　です。
		やさしかった　です。
二	パーティーは　どう　でしたか。	たのしかった　です。
		パーティーは　つまらなかった　です。
三	ばんごはんは　どう　でしたか。	おいしかった　です。
		ばんごはんは　まずかった　です。

11

はなしましょう

Listen to どんなあじ二 はなしましょう and answer the questions in English.

1 What did Asami do during the holiday? How was it? _____

2 What did Yoshi do yesterday and how was it? _____

How about Maki? What did she do and how was it? _____

12

Listen to the CD and write down how the speaker feels about the following. Write in English, or in Japanese if you can.

A なつ休^{やす}み _____

B しけん _____

C すし _____

D クリスマス パーティー^{くりすます ぱーてぃー} _____

E ぶんかさい _____

F 日本ご _____

13

Change these sentences from the present tense (what it is like) to the past tense (what it was like).

A ごはんは おいしい です。 _____

B かいものは つまらない です。 _____

C りょこうは たのしい です。 _____

D 日本ごは やさしい です。 _____

E ほんは おもしろい です。 _____

F コーヒー^{こーひー}は ますい です。 _____

G テスト^{てすと}は むずかしい です。 _____

14

Ask your partner what s/he did and what it was like, using the clues in the pictures. Swap roles after each question.

Example

You: なにを　しましたか。
Partner: 日本ごの　ほんを　よみました。
You: どう　でしたか。
Partner: むずかしかった　です。

15

Emiko has lost her library book. Listen as she retraces her steps over the past week and tries to remember where she left it. Write in the table what she did each day in English, or in Japanese if you can.

月	
火	
水	
木	
金	
土	
日　（きょう）	

16

David has written about his first date. Read his diary entry and write a brief summary of it in English.

はじめての デート

・水曜日の ばんに
サマンサさんに でんわを
しました。

・土曜日に サマンサさんと
スケートに いきました。
でんしゃで いきました。
たのしかった です。

・スケートの あとで
ハンバーガーを たべました。
そして、コーラを のみました。
おいしかった です。

・それから、サマンサさんの
うちに いきました。
サマンサさんと おかあさんと
こわい ビデオを みました。
サマンサさんは こわい
えいが が すき です。
ほんとうに こわかった です。

・いっしょに アイスクリームを
たべました。

17

On separate paper, write an account of your own first date (or what you think it might be like!) in Japanese. Use David's diary in Task 15 as a guide.

Write captions for these holiday pictures. Use at least three sentences.

バーベキューパーティーに
いきました。ハンバーガーを
たべました。おいしかったです。

A _____

_____

_____

B _____

_____

_____

C _____

_____

_____

D _____

_____

_____

E _____

_____

_____

Now write your own sentences about what you did yesterday and draw a picture of it.

_____

_____

_____

_____

_____

_____

Part A

Read Sally's account of her excursion and answer the questions that follow.

11月4日 (火曜日)

きょう、がっこうに いきませんでした。えんそくに
いきました。わたしの 日本ごの クラス<ruby>く<rt>く</rt>ら<rt>ら</rt>す</ruby>は でんしゃで
レストラン<ruby>れ<rt>れ</rt>す<rt>す</rt>と<rt>と</rt>ら<rt>ら</rt>ん</ruby>に いきました。

 わたしは すしと みそしるを たべました。

そして、おちゃを のみました。

すしと みそしるは おいしかった です。

でも、おちゃは まずかった です。

 ひるごはんの あとで、日本の スーパー<ruby>す<rt>す</rt>ー<rt>ー</rt>ぱ<rt>ぱ</rt>ー<rt>ー</rt></ruby>に いきました。

日本の おかしを かいました。たのしかった です。

みそしる miso soup　でも but

A	According to the diary entry what is today's date?
B	Where did they go?
C	Who did she go with?
D	What did she eat?
E	How was it?
F	What did she drink?
G	How was it?
H	What did they do after lunch?
I	What did they buy?

Part B

In your notebook, write an account in Japanese of an excursion you have been on this year.

Ben has written an account of his camping trip for Kidz Times magazine. Read it and answer the questions below in English.

11月23日

きょう、キャンプに いきました。あさ、バスで いきました。
ひるごはんの まえに 日本ごの ゲームを しました。そして、
けんどうの れんしゅうを しました。おもしろかった です。それから、
ひるごはんに パスタと くだものを たべました。まずかった です。
ひるごはんの あとで チョコレートを たべました。そして、じてんしゃに
のりました。サイクリングは たのしかった です。サイクリングの
あとで ばんごはんの りょうりを しました。ばんごはんに にくと
サラダと ごはんを たべました。それから、オレンジジュースを
のみました。ハジョーノくんは にくが きらい です。ぼくは
ハジョーノくんの にくを たべました。おいしかった です。
ばんごはんの あとで、キャンプ ファイヤーを しました。日本人の
おんなのこに あいました。なまえは なおこ です。なおこさんと
ダンスを しました。なおこさんは とても かわいい です。

おんなのこ girl   とても very

A How did they get to the campsite?

B What did they do?

C What did they have for lunch?

D How was it?

E What did they do after lunch?

F What did they have for dinner?

G Why did Ben eat Harjono's dinner?

H What did they do around the camp fire?

I Whom did Ben meet?

Write a letter to your penfriend in Japan telling him or her about your last holiday.
Tell your penfriend:

- When you went
- How you got there
- What it was like

- Where you went
- What you did there
- Whom you met

- Whom you went with
- What you ate and drank
- What you bought there

Add any other information you are able to write in Japanese. Tick off the points above as you write about each one.

22

おしょうゆ クイズ タイム

Circle the correct answer.

A If you want someone to take a picture for you, you will say:
しゃしんを とって ください。
しゃしんを とりました。
しゃしんを たべました。

B If someone says よかったね it means:
- It was yummy wasn't it?
- It was good wasn't it?
- It was difficult wasn't it?

C まいこさん is a
- Girl called Maiko
- Japanese dancer and entertainer
- Policeman

D If someone says あー、そうでしたね they are:
- Surprised
- Disagreeing with you
- Agreeing with you

E カメラ が ありません means:
- I love cameras
- I don't have a camera
- I have a camera

ごちそうさま

I can:
- ☐ ask what someone did on a particular day and respond when someone asks me
- ☐ ask what something was like and respond when someone asks me
- ☐ read and write short sentences which give information about what someone did and what something was like
- ☐ talk about some of the special events in the Japanese school year
- ☐ talk about grammatical concepts which operate across languages, like tense
- ☐ talk about particles and the clues they give me about the sentence in which they are used.

おべんとう　クイズ

1 Circle the correct answer. (3 marks)

A If someone asks you 休み に なにを しましたか they want to know:
- What you are doing in the holidays
- What you did in the holidays
- What sport you play

B どうでしたか means:
- Was it boring?
- Was it raining?
- How was it?

C If someone asks you なんで いきましたか they want to know:
- Where you went?
- How you got there?
- Whom you went with?

2 Select the correct verb from the list to complete each sentence. Then match each sentence with the appropriate picture. (6 marks)

のりました　　　　かきました
ききました　　　　かいました
あいました　　　　みました

A ともだちに

_____

B スケートボード に
（すけーとぼーど）

_____

C えいがを

D てがみを

_____

E チョコレート を
（ちょこれーと）

_____

F おんがくを

_____

3 What Japanese word could you use to describe the following? (6 marks)

A A very expensive shirt you bought

_____

B Very yummy ice-cream you ate

_____

C A very difficult test you did

_____

D A very boring party you went to

_____

E A very interesting book you read

_____

F A very cute cat you saw

4 Answer the following questions truthfully in Japanese. (3 marks)

A 日曜日に なにを しましたか。
（よう）

_____

B だれと しましたか。

_____

C どうでしたか。

_____

5 Write a diary entry giving this information: Wednesday 3 September. I didn't go to school. I went to a tennis match. I went by bus. I watched tennis. I ate ice-cream. It was fun. (6 marks)

_____

_____

6 Write the following words in katakana.(6 marks)

A rollerblades

_____

B taxi

_____

C dance

_____

D party

_____

E cola

_____

F ice-cream

_____

/30

Unit 1

The Obento students

ベンくん	Ben
たかこさん	Takako
ゆきさん	Yuki
トニーくん	Tony
ハジョーノくん	Harjono
なかむら せんせい	Mr. Nakamura (Teacher)
けんいちくん	Kenichi
ゆうすけくん	Yuusuke
みなさん	everyone
ケイトさん	Kate
エマさん	Emma

....

いって	say
いって ください	say, please
おはようございます	Good morning
かいて	write or draw
かいて ください	write or draw please
きいて	listen
きいて ください	listen please
こんにちは	Hello/Good afternoon
さようなら	Goodbye
しずかにして！	be quiet
しずかに してください	be quiet please
すわって	sit down
すわって ください	sit down please
たって	stand up
たって ください	stand up please
ドアを あけて	open the door
ドアを あけて ください	open the door please
ドアを しめて	shut the door
ドアを しめて ください	shut the door please
どうぞよろしく	Pleased to meet you
にほん	Japan
ぼく	I (boys)
また、あした	See you tomorrow
まどを あけて	open the window
まどを あけて ください	open the window please
まどを しめて	shut the window
まどを しめて ください	shut the window please
みせて	show it
みせて ください	show it please
みて	look
みて ください	look please
よんで	read
よんで ください	read please
わたし	I

_____   _____

_____   _____

_____   _____

_____   _____

_____   _____

Unit 2

Ages

一さい です／いっさい	1 year old
二さい です／にさい	2 years old
三さい です／さんさい	3 years old
四さい です／よんさい	4 years old
五さい です／ごさい	5 years old
六さい です／ろくさい	6 years old
七さい です／ななさい	7 years old
八さい です／はっさい	8 years old
九さい です／きゅうさい	9 years old
十さい です／じゅっさい	10 years old
十一さい です／じゅういっさい	11 years old
十二さい です／じゅうにさい	12 years old
十三さい です／じゅうさんさい	13 years old
十四さい です／じゅうよんさい	14 years old
十五さい です／じゅうごさい	15 years old
十六さい です／じゅうろくさい	16 years old
十七さい です／じゅうななさい	17 years old
十八さい です／じゅうはっさい	18 years old
十九さい です／じゅうきゅうさい	19 years old
二十 です／はたち	20 years old

Numbers from zero to 20

○／ゼロ or れい	0
一／いち	1
二 ／に	2
三／さん	3
四／し or よん	4
五／ご	5
六／ろく	6
七／しち or なな	7
八／はち	8
九／きゅう or く	9
十／じゅう	10
十一／じゅういち	11
十二／じゅうに	12
十三／じゅうさん	13
十四／じゅうし or じゅうよん	14
十五／じゅうご	15
十六／じゅうろく	16
十七／じゅうしち or じゅうなな	17
十八／じゅうはち	18
十九／じゅうきゅう or じゅうく	19
二十／にじゅう	20

_____ _____

_____ _____

_____ _____

_____ _____

_____ _____

Unit 3

アメリカ	America
アメリカ人	American
インドネシア	Indonesia
インドネシア人	Indonesian

オークランド	Auckland	おかあさん	Mother
オーストラリア	Australia	おじいさん	Grandfather
オーストラリア人	Australian	おとうさん	Father
カナダ	Canada	おとうと	younger brother
カナダ人	Canadian	おにいさん	older brother
シドニー	Sydney	おねえさん	older sister
ジャカルター	Jakarta	おばあさん	Grandmother
とうきょう	Tokyo	きゅうにん／九人	9 people
トロント	Toronto	きんぎょ	goldfish
日本	Japan	ごにん／五人	5 people
日本人	Japanese	さんにん／三人	3 people
ニュージーランド	New Zealand	しちにん／七人	7 people
ニュージーランド人	New Zealander	じゅうにん／十人	10 people
パース	Perth	とり	bird
メルボルン	Melbourne	なんにん／なん人	How many people?
		ねこ	cat

_____ _____

_____ _____

_____ _____

_____ _____

_____ _____

Unit 4

あかちゃん	baby	はちにん／八人	8 people
あひる	duck	ひとり／一人	1 person
いぬ	dog	ふたり／二人	2 people
いもうと	younger sister	へび	snake
うさぎ	rabbit	よにん／四人	4 people
うま	horse	ろくにん／六人	6 people
		わたし／ぼく	me

_____ _____

_____ _____

_____ _____

_____ _____

Unit 5

あひる	duck
いぬ	dog
うさぎ	rabbit
うま	horse
うるさい	noisy
えさ	food for animals
おおきい	big
おべんとう	packed meal
おもしろい	interesting/funny
かわいい	cute
きんぎょ	goldfish
くさ	grass
こわい	scary
さかな	fish
ちいさい	small
とり	bird
にく	meat
ねこ	cat
パン	bread
へび	snake
ぼくの	My (boys)
ミルク	milk
みず	water
やさい	vegetables
わたしの	My (girls)

_____   _____

_____   _____

_____   _____

Unit 6

アイスクリーム	ice cream
あさごはん	breakfast
あまり	not much
いいえ、あんまり...。	No, not really.
おかし	sweets
おかず	side dish
おちゃ	green tea
おべんとう	packed / boxed meal (obento)
オレンジ ジュース	orange juice
カレーライス	curry rice
くだもの	fruit
ケーキ	cake
こうちゃ	English tea
コーヒー	coffee
コーラ	coke
コーンフレーク	cornflakes
ごはん	rice
さかな	fish
サラダ	salad
サンドイッチ	sandwiches
ぜんぜん	not at all
ソーセージ	sausages
たべます	eat
たべません	don't eat

たまご	eggs		
チーズ	cheese		
チキン	chicken		
チョコレート	chocolate		
トースト	toast		
ときどき	sometimes		
にく	meat		
のみます	drink		
のみません	don't drink		
はい、すき です。	Yes, I like it.		
はい、だいすき です。	Yes, I love it.		
パスタ	pasta		
ばんごはん	dinner		
ハンバーガー	hamburgers		
ピザ	pizza		
ひるごはん	lunch		
まいにち	everyday		
みず	water		
ミルク	milk		
やさい	vegetable		
よく	often		

_____ _____

_____ _____

_____ _____

_____ _____

_____ _____

Unit 7

いちがつ／一月	January
いつか／五日	5th
うんどうかい	sports carnival
えんそく	excursion
かようび／火曜日	Tuesday
キャンプ	camp
きんようび／金曜日	Friday
くがつ／九月	September
げつようび／月曜日	Monday
ごがつ／五月	May
ここのか／九日	9th
さんがつ／三月	March
さんじゅういちにち／三十一日	31st
さんじゅうにち／三十日	30th
しがつ／四月	April
しちがつ／七月	July
じゅういちがつ／十一月	November
じゅういちにち／十一日	11th
じゅうがつ／十月	October
じゅうくにち／十九日	19th
じゅうごにち／十五日	15th
じゅうさんにち／十三日	13th
じゅうしちにち／十七日	17th
じゅうにがつ／十二月	December
じゅうににち／十二日	12th
じゅうはちにち／十八日	18th
じゅうよっか／十四日	14th

じゅうろくにち／十六日	16th	もくようび／木曜日	Thursday
すいえいたいかい	swimming carnival	ようか／八日	8th
すいようび／水曜日	Wednesday	よっか／四日	4th
たんじょうび	birthday	ろくがつ／六月	June
ダンスパーティー	dance		
ついたち／一日	1st		
テスト	test		
とおか／十日	10th		
どようび／土曜日	Saturday		
なのか／七日	7th		
にがつ／二月	February		

Unit 8

にじゅういちにち／二十一日	21st	インドネシア ご	Indonesian
にじゅうくにち／二十九日	29th	えいご	English
にじゅうごにち／二十五日	25th	オーストラリアン フットボール	Australian Rules football
にじゅうさんにち／二十三日	23rd	おんがく	music
にじゅうしちにち／二十七日	27th	ギター	guitar
にじゅうににち／二十二日	22nd	クリケット	cricket
にじゅうはちにち／二十八日	28th	ゴルフ	golf
にじゅうよっか／二十四日	24th	コンピューター	computers
にじゅうろくにち／二十六日	26th	サーフィン	surfing
にちようび／日曜日	Sunday	サッカー	soccer
パーティー	party	じょうば	horse-riding
はちがつ／八月	August	スケート	skating
はつか／二十日	20th	すいえい	swimming
ふつか／二日	2nd	ソフトボール	softball
休み	holiday	どくしょ	reading
みっか／三日	3rd	ネットボール	netball
むいか／六日	6th		

バスケットボール	basketball	じてんしゃ	bicycle
バレーボール	volleyball	しゅうまつ	weekend
ピアノ	piano	しんかんせん	bullet train
フランス ご	French	スクーター	scooter
ホッケー	hockey	タクシー	taxi
やきゅう	baseball	テニスの しあい	a game of tennis
ラグビー	rugby	デパート	a department store
りょうり	cooking	でんしゃ	train
ローラーブレード	rollerblading	ともだち	a friend
		ともだちの うち	a friend's house
_____	_____	バス	bus
_____	_____	バレーボールの しあい	a game of volleyball
_____	_____	パーティー	a party
_____	_____	ピクニック	a picnic
_____	_____	ひこうき	airplane

Unit 9

あした	tomorrow	ひとりで／一人で	by myself
あるいて	on foot	フットボールの しあい	a game of football
うみ	the beach	フェリー	ferry
えいが	a film	まち	town
おばあさんの うち	Grandma's house	やきゅうの しあい	a game of baseball
かぞく	family	ゆきさん	Yuki
がっこう	school	ゆきさんの くるま	Yuki's car
からての しあい	a game of karate	レストラン	a restaurant
きょう	today		
けんどうの しあい	a game of kendo	_____	_____
コンサート	a concert	_____	_____
サッカーの しあい	a game of soccer	_____	_____
		_____	_____

Unit 10

CD	CD
DVD	DVD
E メール	email
MD プレーヤ	MD player
えいが	movies
おんがく	music
かいもの	shopping
カラオケ	karaoke
くつ	shoes
けいたい	mobile
けいたいでんわ	mobile telephone
ざっし	magazines
しゅくだい	homework
しんぶん	newspaper
そして	And also we/I 〜
それから	And then we/I 〜
チャット	Internet chat
てがみ	letter
デジカメ	digital camera
テレビ	TV
でんわ	telephone
にっき	diary
日本ごの べんきょう	Japanese study
パーティー	party
ピアノの れんしゅう	piano practice
ビデオ	video
ビデオクリップ	video clip
ファッション ざっし	fashion magazines
本	book
まんが	comics
やきゅうの しあい	baseball match
ラジオ	radio
れんしゅう	practice

_____	_____
_____	_____
_____	_____
_____	_____
_____	_____

Unit 11

あさ	in the morning
あしたの あさ	tomorrow morning
あしたの ばん	tomorrow evening
あとで	later
いきましょう	let's go
おいしい	delicious
おもしろい	interesting/funny
かいましょう	let's buy
かきましょう	let's write
がっこうの あとで	after school
がっこうの まえに	before school
ききましょう	let's listen
金曜日の ばん	friday night
しましょう	let's do
たかい	expensive

たのしい	fun	うみ	beach
たべましょう	let's eat	うるさかった	was noisy
つまらない	boring	えいが	movie
のみましょう	let's drink	えんそく	excursion
ひまなときに	in your spare time	おいしかった	was delicious
ひるやすみに	at lunchtime	おおきかった	was big
まずい	tastes awful	おてら	temple
みましょう	let's look	おみやげ	souvenir
むずかしい	difficult	おもしろかった	was interesting
やさしい	easy	おんがく	music
やすい	cheap	かいました。	I bought 〜
よみましょう	let's read	かいませんでした。	I didn't buy 〜
よる	at night	かいもの	shopping
		かきました。	I wrote 〜
_____	_____	かきませんでした。	I didn't write 〜
_____	_____	かぞく	family
_____	_____	かわいかった	was cute
_____	_____	ききました。	I listened to 〜
_____	_____	ききませんでした。	I didn't listen to 〜

Unit 12

		きのう	Yesterday
（に）あいました。	I met 〜	きんようびのばん	On Friday night
（に）あいませんでした。	I didn't meet 〜	くつ	shoes
（に）いきました。	I went to 〜	ケーキ	cake
（に）いきませんでした。	I didn't go to 〜	コーラ	coke
（に）のりました。	I took 〜	こわかった	was scary
（に）のりませんでした。	I didn't take 〜	さくぶん	composition
あさ	In the morning	しけん	exam
うま	horse	じてんしゃ	bicycle

しました。	I did ～	まずかった	tasted awful
しませんでした。	I didn't do ～	まんが	comic
しゃしん	photo(s)	みました。	I saw ～
しゅくだい	homework	みませんでした。	I didn't see ～
しんかんせん	bullet train	むずかしかった	was difficult
しんぶん	newspaper	やさしかった	was easy
たかかった	was expensive	やすかった	was cheap
たかこさん	Takako	やすみ	holiday
たのしかった	was fun	やすみに	On holiday/s
たべました。	I ate ～	よみました。	I read ～
たべませんでした。	I didn't eat ～	よみませんでした。	I didn't read ～
たんじょうびに	On (someone's) birthday	ラジオ	radio
ちいさかった	was little/small	りょこう	trip
つまらなかった	was boring	れんしゅう	practice
てがみ	letter	ローラーコースター	roller coaster
テニス	tennis		
テレビ	TV		
でんわ	telephone		
としょかん	library		
ともだち	friend(s)		
とりました。	I took ～		
とりませんでした。	I didn't take ～		
にっき	diary		
のみました。	I drank ～		
のみませんでした。	I didn't drink ～		
本	At night		
ビデオ	video		
ほん	book		

Student Audio CD tracklist